Praise for *The Best of the S*

"Some of the happiest moments of my writing life have been spent in the company of writers whose work is included in these pages. They all brought their A-game to this fabulous collection, and at our house it is going on a shelf next to its honored predecessors. The only thing that saddens me is that the large-hearted William Gay is not around to absorb some of the love that shines through every word."

—Steve Yarbrough, multiple award winning author and PEN/Faulkner Award finalist (*Prisoners of War*) whose latest novel, *The Unmade World*, won the 2019 Massachusetts Book Award in Fiction

"*The Best of the Shortest* takes the reader on a fast-paced adventure from familiar back roads to the jungles of Viet Nam; from muddy southern creek banks to the other side of the world, touching on themes as beautiful as love and as harsh as racism. However dark or uplifting, you are guaranteed to enjoy the ride."

—Bob Zellner, Civil Rights activist and author of *The Wrong Side of Murder Creek* (memoir; became the film *Son of the South*, directed by Barry Alexander Brown, produced by Spike Lee) and the upcoming *Freedom Road* (memoir sequel)

"I had some of the best times of my life meeting, drinking and chatting with the writers in this book, times matched only by the hours I spent reading their books. This collection showcases a slice of Southern literature in all its complicated, glorious genius. Anyone who likes good writing will love it."

—Clay Risen, author of *The Crowded Hour: Theodore Roosevelt, the Rough Riders and the Dawn of the American Century*

Other books by the editors:

Suzanne Hudson

Opposable Thumbs
In a Temple of Trees
In the Dark of the Moon
All the Way to Memphis
Shoe Burnin' Season: a Womanifesto (pseudonym R.P. Saffire)
The Fall of the Nixon Administration (a comic novel)

Mandy Haynes

Walking the Wrong Way Home
Sharp as a Serpent's Tooth: Eva and Other Stories
Oliver

Joe Formichella

Schopenhauer's Maxim
Waffle House Rules
Scarpete Stories
The Wreck of the Twilight Limited
Whores for Life: Scatolo's and Other Stories
*Lumpers, Longnecks, and One-Eyed Jacks: a '70s Recipe for a
       Rainy Day*

Nonfiction:
Staying Ahead of the Posse
Murder Creek
*Here's to You, Jackie Robinson: the Legend of the
       Prichard Mohawks/ A Condition of Freedom*

The Best of the Shortest:
a Southern Writers Reading Reunion

Edited by Suzanne Hudson
with Mandy Haynes and Joe Formichella

Livingston Press

The University of West Alabama

The UNIVERSITY of
WEST ALABAMA

ISBN 13: 978-1-60489-351-9   hardcover
ISBN 13: 978-1-60489-352-6   trade paper
ISBN 13: 978-1-60489-362-5   e-book
Library of Congress Cataloguing in progress: 2023939125

This is a work of fiction: You know the rest. Resemblances to persons
living or dead is coincidental. Livingston Press is a non-profit organiza-
tion. Contributions are tax-deductibe and welcome.

Cover photo by Maude Schuyler Clay: treeline at Longstreet Woods
near Vance, Mississippi

"Morning. A hot August sun was smoking up over a wavering treeline.
Such drunks as were still about struggled up beneath the malign heat
slowly and painfully as if they moved in altered time or through an
atmosphere thickening to amber. The glade was absolutely breezeless
and the threat of the sun imminent and horrific. The sweep of the sun
lengthened."
            —from *The Long Home*, William Gay's first novel

Back cover art, *The Harrikin*, courtesy of J.M. White, archivist of the
William Gay estate

Cover design by Taylor Michael D'Amico, streetheatmedia.com

Proofreading: Annsley Johnsey, Savannah Beams, Kaitlynn Clark, Tri-
cia Taylor, Brooke Barger

Special thanks to Jim Davis
Special thanks also to Waterhole Branch Productions

Credits, in chronological order of authors' appearances:

"Married Love," "What I Think When Someone Uses the Word 'Pussy' as a Synonym for 'Weak'," and "Goner" *Heating and Cooling: 52 Micro-Memoirs*, W.W. Norton & Company, Inc., 2017

"Who is the Real Pig Boy?" from *Pig Boy's Wicked Bird: A Memoir*, Chicago Review Press, Inc.,2004

"Chitlins" *Stories from the Blue Moon Café*, vol. IV, edited by Sonny Brewer, MacAdam/Cage, 2005

"When Gravity Lets Go" *Fiction Southeast* (online), April 4, 2019

"Slacabamorinico," "The World's Greatest Pants," and "Disneyland" from *The Girl in the Fall-Away Dress*, University of Massachusetts, Amherst, 2001

"Teach Me" first read on "Texas Standard," a National Public Radio show; the text is printed on their web site: www.texasstandard.org

"Rehab" *Georgia State University Review*, fall 2001; *Stories from the Blue Moon Café*, vol. IV, edited by Sonny Brewer, MacAdam/Cage, 2005 "The Green Woman" *Portland Magazine*, 2000; and *Climbing Mount Cheaha*, edited by Don Noble, Livingston Press, 2004

"Nearing Mars," *Fort Smith Historical Society Journal*, vol. 43, no. 2, September, 2019

Second Sluthood republished as *Shoe Burnin' Season: A Womanifesto*; edited by Suzanne Hudson, Waterhole Branch Productions, 2018

"Whiskey Blues" *Garden & Gun* magazine, 2023

"White Trash Fishing" *The Raleigh News and Observer*; *The Alumni Grill*, edited by William Gay and Suzanne Kingsbury, MacAdam/Cage, 2004

"Three Days at the US Open" *Tennis View* magazine

"The Walker" from the forthcoming book *Beyond Tam O'Shanter*

"The Boys" *Cutleaf* and *The Cutleaf Reader*, vol. 2 anthology

"Leaving Vermont" from *Lumpers, Longnecks, and One-Eyed Jacks: A 70s Recipe for a Rainy Day*, Waterhole Branch Productions, 2019

"Left Behind" *Stories from the Blue Moon Café*, vol. I, edited by Sonny Brewer, MacAdam/Cage, 2002

"Snakebit" Winter 2001 issue of *Fourteen Hills: The SFSU Review*

"Birds of a Feather" *Topic* magazine

"Never-Ending" *Flash*: The International Short-Short Story magazine; vol.6, no. 2, October, 2013

"The Thing with Feathers" *Stories from the Blue Moon Café*, vol. IV, edited by Sonny Brewer, MacAdam/Cage, 2005; *All the Way to Memphis*, edited by Wendy Reed, River's Edge Media, 2014

"Welcome To Monroe" *A Kudzu Christmas: Twelve Mysterious Tales*; edited by Jim Gilbert and Gail Waller; River City Publishing, 2005

"Dear Friend" *Stories from the Blue Moon Café*, vol. IV, edited by Sonny Brewer, MacAdam/Cage, 2005

This collection is dedicated to the memory of William Gay, the inspiration for the first Southern Writers Reading.

Photo credit: Maude Schuyler Clay

William Gay, squat-sitting on his heels, country style

And to the memory of Southern Writers Reading Alumni who are with William in the Everafter . . .

William Cobb
Wayne Greenhaw
Tom Kelley
Barbara Robinette Moss
Carl T. Smith
Brad Watson

CONTENTS

INTRODUCTION
Suzanne Hudson

The incomparable William Gay not only inspired it. He kept coming back.

Southern Writers Reading was the literary scene gone rogue, upsetting the apple carts of more than a couple of self-satisfied editors in the region. It was the anti-establishment strain of the literary family, the kids in the back of the classroom shooting spitballs, lobbing rotten apples, thumbing their noses at grammatical prudes. And William had nothing but disdain for posturing and preening, academic airs, mercenary social climbing, obsequious ass-kissing. And limousines. No wonder he kept returning.

1998-2008: these were literary magic years, with Big Daddy Sonny Brewer bringing the juju, along with partners-in-crime like Jim Gilbert, Kyle Jennings, Skip Jones, and Martin Lanaux. The community came alive, venues volunteered, folks opened their homes to lodge authors, throw parties, banquets, lunches and brunches, and the ABC store did a very brisk business. The weekend's events all fell under the umbrella of Southern Writers Reading.

Why "Southern"? There's been much debate over the last couple of decades about whether the classification should even exist anymore. For my own self, I just know that when I was doing research for my 2003 novel *In a Temple of Trees*, I explored some very dark, *Deliverance*-like parts of West Alabama that took me right back to my childhood days in southwest Georgia—in the 1950s. Places where time has stopped. My protective guide took me to dives and honky tonks and drove me around with a man and his six-year-old son, *both* of whom enthusiastically chewed and spat tobacco. We visited a woman in jail accused of carving her boyfriend's rectum out with a fish scaling knife. I witnessed an elderly African American man address a teenage white boy as "sir," and not in an ironic way. Confederate flags were not uncommon.

No matter. The truth is you didn't really have to be Southern to participate in SWR. Maybe you were born here and moved across the world. Maybe you were firmly rooted in Pennsylvania but wrote about Georgia. Maybe you didn't even write fiction. Sonny considered songwriting as part of the spirit and often featured music as well. Maybe, like my husband, you were born in upstate New York but left right after high school to live on the Gulf Coast for almost fifty years now. Sonny could justify calling just about anybody a "Southern writer." Mainly you had to be very talented and a good person on top of that. Divas and pricks and grammar/editing Nazis did not get invited to come back.

Authors and readers attended the weekend's events together, socialized, appreciated one another, that give and take so vital to any of the arts. As long as the authors could get here from nearby or far-flung places on their own dime, they would not want for room and board. Or the aforementioned likker (a topic addressed within these pages by the likes of Rick Bragg, Beth Ann Fennelly, Ron Rash, and George Singleton). It was not about profit, or building a "brand," or catering to egos (although a few popped up from time to time). It was not about rigidity, rules, or one-upmanship. It was, as Sonny would say, organic. And fun. The kind of good energy that only the best ethereal juju can Karmalize. That's why authors and readers made it an annual pilgrimage—the good, good, good; good vibrations.

Matter of fact, that very last year, when there *were* undercurrents of "branding" and such, grasps at control from beyond (as tends to happen with any good thing), might have been what undid it. Partially.

No matter. We decided to undo the undid.

We've long spoken about a reunion, a re-creation of the experience, the magic—one last hurrah, we reasoned, as many of us are on the downhill slope, some already beyond the here and now. Why not gather up and raise a glass, whether warm milk or straight moonshine, to those we miss, and to each other as well?

We made this decision in the fall of 2022. And, because SWR was/is so organic and perfect and spur-of-the-moment, we decided to aim for November, 2023. And, hey, why not do an oral history? And a book—an anthology, invite anyone who's ever been a panelist at SWR to contribute a piece, and bring it out for the big party?

Are you out of your freaking mind? Can't be done. There will be too many contributors, too much to edit, the book will be too fat and expensive.

Not if we put limits on word count. Remember, these are pros, they won't possibly need much editing, and I hear the American public has such a short attention span they'd prefer short pieces.

But you have to have a theme, and you can't just mish-mash random categories into a wad of literary goo.

Watch us. Besides, there *is* a theme: short. The best of the shortest. Under 1500 words.

But there's not enough time! Publishing takes two years, maybe—if you're lucky.

That was the 20th century. The industry is changing. And if we can find ourselves an edgy, provocative, adventurous publisher . . .

Enter Joe Taylor at Livingston Press, the most honest, ethical, funny, and daring publisher we've ever known. And he was game. Of course.

*But who will put this all together? The reunion weekend, the hosts, the parties, **the anthology**?*

Sonny allowed he did not have the drive or the inclination to take charge. Besides, he didn't want the stress, rightly so, leading up to and after his double bypass in December of '22.

So I volunteered. Yours truly. Little ol' me. I'm a retired school marm/counselor, have all the time in the world, spent thirty-one years in public education, mostly middle school, so I can damn sure herd some cats. The real question was, could Sonny keep his hands off?

I'm fond of saying that Sonny Brewer has been a pain in my ass for going on fifty years. That's how long he's been my editor—the Lou Grant to my Mary Tyler Moore. When one is so used to being The Decider in Chief, it can be hard to let go. But Sonny has mellowed over time, embraces the Zen that soothes his ticker.

Back in the day, around the turn of this century, when I suggested he include more women in his anthologies, out popped what he calls his "inner troll," commencing to cuss and tell me to mind my own damn business. "I'm the goddamn editor! I'll do whatever the hell I want!"

He made me cry.

But when the inner troll receded, as it always did, there would be hugs all around, and the man with the big heart would always be there to support me and the writing community.

I do love him.

(Not in *that* way.)

And I've had a fabulous time with this project, with plenty of help from Sonny, along with my co-editors Joe Formichella (also my husband, whom I **do** love in *that* way) and Mandy Haynes, a power-house of a somebody, who brings her own exuberant juju to anything she does.

We rounded up the vast majority of the authors. There were some we simply could not find or did not have the luxury of time to track down. A couple declined, maybe expecting honoraria or some kind of paycheck that was not to be (although here is a good place to point out that all royalties/profits will be donated to the Fairhope Center for the Writing Arts, one of the many dominoes SWR knocked into motion). Some were just plain too busy dealing with work and life. Others simply didn't have short-short in their repertoires, so we pulled some excerpts, some essays, asked them to reach under their mattresses.

Several of them consented for me to carve on their work. That's when you know you're dealing with pros sans egos. I believe Karen Spears Zacharias's words were, "Whittle away!" And I was mightily proud of a sampling I pulled from Ravi Howard's *Like Trees, Walking* (a novel inspired by the 1981 lynching of Michael Donald—a young man of color—in Mobile, Alabama; no, that is not a typo: *1981*), but there was a contractual glitch with the publisher, so that was not to be included. I only mention it here because Ravi deserves a mention. Get that book. Now.

Since it's always been a point of irritation to me, ever since college, that I did not see many women's names in tables of contents of short story collections, still don't (unless it is a specifically woman-centered collection); and since I was getting multiple pieces from most of the SWR women; and since the pieces were DAMN good, I decided what the hell? To quote Sonny Brewer, "I'm the goddamn editor." I'll showcase the women as much as possible. You will see most of the female names repeated in the table of contents, a few of them multiple times.

Not difficult to do with a badass like Beth Ann Fennelly and her prickly funny or gut-wrenchingly devastating micro-memoirs. Or a badass like Janet Nodar, who had to use the name J.C. Nodar before "Rehab" was accepted for publication (after multiple submissions as "Janet") and whose story "The Green Woman" gives me goosebumps.

As a dog lover, I know that Pia Z. Ehrhardt's "It's Been Six Months" gets it right: our canine friends process grief, look for the souls they love, have a difficult time understanding. The same goes for our feathered pets. Just ask Abbott Kahler (formerly Karen Abbott).

Michelle Richmond calls out racism with a middle finger to a certain place in "Slacabamorinico," and Patricia Foster powerfully understates it in "Silence." They are all badass, these women: Lynn Pruett, Cassandra King, Jennifer Paddock, Joshilyn Jackson.

Like Karen Spears Zacharias, Bev Marshall trusted me with editing a couple of excerpts from her powerful memoir about being a Vietnam era military wife, and R.P. Saffire gives a counterpoint on marriage in general, skewering the institution as only she can.

Since I did not want to be accused of hypocrisy, I carved up one of my shortest stories, "The Thing with Feathers" by at least one third to bring it down under 1500 words. However, I went a little easy on the length of Suzanne Kingsbury's submissions, simply because William Gay, her once upon a time love and her always beloved friend, still talks to her, from the Other Side.

I first met William Gay in 1999. He was squat-sitting on his heels, country style, leaning against the front outside of Sonny's bookstore, Over the Transom, smoking a cigarette. Before he even said hello, he said:

"I read your story. In *Penthouse*. I liked it. I entered that same contest. I got rejected right away. Mine wasn't a very good story." He spoke haltingly, with a profound rural Tennessee accent that was like buttah.

The winning story announcement he was referencing was in 1977. He had been "toiling away in obscurity," as fan Stephen King said of him, for about thirty years. We became friends, took up a correspondence of snail mail, an occasional phone call, and crossed paths at festivals, conferences, and such. He came and stayed with us for a couple of weeks, to help me edit my first collection of short stories, *Opposable Thumbs*. I treasure the pages with his notes in the margins, and there's one particular sentence in there that is *all* William.

Having met my manfriend of twenty years at the time, and then my next (interim) escort, followed by my destined-to-be-husband Joe; and having talked books and politics with all of them, William pronounced more than once to me: "You have impeccable taste in men." The thought of that always makes me smile.

William bonded with Sonny and many cohorts in the literary community—right off the bat with Tommy Franklin, who along with many of the authors in this collection, knew William as a good friend. Yet another reason it is so fitting to dedicate these pages to him. I hope he enjoys them. Let us know, would you, Kingsbury?

Tom Franklin, whose "My Wife's Good Looking Friends" made me laugh before I thought, "Wait, what?" and just wanted to give the poor guy a hug. George Singleton also made us laugh, along with William and Tommy and many more, in many a bar on the literary circuit, as he does with "Everyone Said Nothing." Daniel Wallace, who, when asked for a story, wrote that the SWR crew was "like family" and let me use his disturbing and beautiful "Welcome to Monroe." His is another story I fudged on the length, on account of the fact that Daniel Wallace is the nicest man on the planet.

It was fun to include guys who were just kids (to us elders) back when they were invited to be on a panel at SWR. I have seen former newbie David Wright Faladé's short story byline in no less than *The New Yorker*. Here he offers an editorial on whiteness and racism, "Teach Me," written after the murder of George Floyd. And yet.

That whippersnapper James Whorton, Jr. has three novels under his belt and gives us a "Creative Writing" experience through the eyes of a rudderless twenty-something. And that young'un Jason Headley? Even though he's joined the ranks of the film industry, he has gifted us with the truly disturbing "An Explosion When You See One." When another one of the kids, Bobby—Robert Gatewood—submitted his "Such is Man," I texted him: "I have always had a soft spot in my heart for the harsh shit. Thank you." He texted back, "Ha." I could be wrong, but somehow I don't think Gatewood sends too many "ha" texts.

We have flash fiction from Sidney Thompson and Bret Anthony Johnston, essays from Doug Kelley and Mac Walcott, an excerpt from Michael Morris's novel in progress, *The King of Flora*, while Theodore Pitsios's novel excerpt is from the published *Walking In the Light*. Joe Formichella's "Leaving Vermont" excerpt is from his novel *Lumpers, Longnecks, and One-Eyed Jacks: A 70s Recipe for a Rainy Day*, a national finalist for an Indie Book Award that was released in early 2020, just in time to be squashed by COVID.

Sonny Brewer and Marlin Barton explore complex relationships between fathers and sons in their short fiction, "With These Rings" and "When Gravity Lets Go," respectively. The vast majority of submissions stand alone. Several are little morsels, like the samples set out in stores, stuck with toothpicks, to tease your taste buds into buying the product. There is something for everyone.

As for hard core "regional" / "Southern" fare, we get pigs from Doug Crandell and chitlins from Robert St. John. Dayne Sherman serves up a cold dish of revenge for a murdered Treeing Feist. Frank Turner Hollon's trailer dweller lives with hordes of cats until his ex-woman exits, leaving just one cat behind, a cat in a dire situation. And Ron Rash takes us "White Trash Fishing." Can it get more "regional"?

Well, yes. Daren Wang pulled out a "lost chapter" from his civil war / abolition novel, *The Hidden Light of Northern Fires*. He explains: "It shouldn't take too much imagination for readers to recognize that Shelby Bell [a slave owner] is named after another famous Southerner named Shelby. Shelby Foote's smirking storytelling about the gallant and witty generals of the lost cause during Ken Burns' *The Civil War* series is almost unwatchable today. It galled me as I wrote the point of view of a documented feminist abolitionist like Mary Willis, and I really enjoyed having her way with him in this scene. . . I was told by a friend of Mr. Foote's that he was high throughout the entire filming. That makes me dislike him slightly less."

The story I placed in the middling part of the book, "Whiskey Blues" by Rick Bragg, is not 1500 words. It's many times that. And it is wonderful. I would not dare ask to edit it down. He has a freaking Pulitzer Prize, so no, I don't think so. Bragg is also the only male who has two pieces in the book. His short-short "Dear Friend" is the final piece, not only because it is Rick Damn Bragg, but it is intentionally placed there to give us a lift after going down a disturbing road with Daniel Wallace. And it is a letter to his friend, Sonny Brewer.

And nobody had better say it's not fair or it doesn't fit.

Southern Writers Reading was also as hodgepodgy and unpredictable.

(Again, I'm the goddamn editor.)

Joe Taylor was very generous, allowing us creative control over the cover, for example. Maude Schuyler Clay, an alumna of SWR, joined us in 2007 with her book of photography. She is the Real Deal (yet another badass) and offered us a choice of photos for the front cover. And, as a friend of William's, she had a cornucopia of images from which we got the perfect one for the dedication page: William, squat-sitting on his heels, country style.

We wanted one of William's paintings for the back cover, just because, and yet another generous source, the "literary archaeologist" and curator of all things William Gay, Michael White, accommodated. His cohort and fellow editor, Dawn Major, contributed William's beautiful words and her commentary on the painting they call *The Harrikin*.

Finally, my graphic designer cousin-in-law, Taylor Michael D'Amico, put it all together. This truly has been a "Hey, kids, let's put on a show!" a la Andy Hardy kind of thing (and semi-referenced as such by Jim Gilbert in the Afterword, a fuller literary history, "The Café Under the Transom").

If you are now holding this book in your hands, you are likely at the 2023 "reunion"; and if it's anything like it's supposed to be, you will appreciate a few quotes from assorted news articles and such over the magical years.

From Clay Risen, writing for the *Nashville Scene* (Nov. 18, 2004):

"In most of small-town Alabama, a bunch of writers cavorting and drinking late at night would be a rare find. But not in Fairhope, at least not on the weekend before Thanksgiving . . ."

" . . . the driving force behind Southern Writers Reading is

Sonny Brewer, a former real-estate agent, used car salesman, and novelist (his first book, *The Poet of Tolstoy Park*, is due out next spring) who now owns Over the Transom Books in Fairhope . . ."

From Jim Gilbert's "The Café Under the Transom:"

[California publisher David] "Poindexter would later describe the experience as 'falling into a nest' of wordsmithing talent. 'I don't get it,' [his editor Pat] Walsh confided to me after just the first night, 'We do this in San Francisco, we get seven people. You do it here in this little Alabama town, and a hundred plus show up.' I didn't have an answer for him then, and I wouldn't have one now, other than we picked the right battle, some kind of magic, a celestial alignment, whatever, it worked."

From Janet Nodar, writing for *Southern Breeze* magazine (2006):

" . . . as idiosyncratic a literary event as has ever existed . . . Founder Sonny Brewer calls SWR a 'literary slugfest' and 'literature as spectator sport.'

"At SWR, you will not find breakout sessions on Writing the Perfect Query Letter or What You Should Know About Publishing Contracts . . . these topics have nothing to do with the discipline, frustration, and serious joy of writing well.

"SWR is not about the business of writing.

"It isn't an academic event, either.

" . . . It is about Southern storytelling.

"As local historian, critic, and writer John Sledge puts it, SWR is rooted in Faulkner, in a gritty blue-collar literary tradition of 'hard stuff, beautifully written.'"

Again, from Risen:

"These days it's conventional wisdom in many publishing circles to proclaim, against massive evidence to the contrary, that Southern literature is long dead. Simply trying to convince editors outside the South that such writing even exists is a tough job. I've had pitches rejected out of hand with a note informing me that Southern literature died with Walker Percy. Perhaps this is the sort of trans-regional, cosmopolitan culture that has overtaken the country via television and the Internet; perhaps it is just an unwillingness to recognize that the South—in contrast with, say, the Mid-Atlantic states—could even have a distinctive literary voice anymore. Such skeptics might think twice, however, after seeing the folks gathered for Southern Writers Reading. Granted, community isn't literature. But the sort of camaraderie and networking on display in Fairhope, Alabama, every November plays a big part in helping a literary spirit grow."

Here's to that spirit.

And to the spirits of those on the dedication page (which, included with this introduction, comes in at about 3,564 words. Rule-breaking. Of course. It makes perfect Southern Writers Reading sense.)

THE PERFECT GIFT
Cassandra King

My son was seven months old when I gave him his first book. In spite of his tender age, it was not one of those cloth or plastic kinds made for babies, oh, no. The book was a beautifully illustrated and expensive edition of Beatrix Potter's *Tales of Peter Rabbit*. Like most young, inexperienced mothers, I was convinced that my son was a genius. After all, he'd already said his first word, "light," pointing to a lamp. Enough evidence for me—he was ready to read. I sat him down next to me on the sofa and placed the book into his chubby little hands. He examined it front and back, turning it every which way. He opened the pages and patted the pictures happily. Then, looking up at me for approval, he raised the book to his mouth and began to eat it.

It was an impulse I understood completely. There are some books so yummy looking that I would devour them if I could. For me, reading has always been a sensual experience. I lust after books. I love everything about them, how they look, how they feel, and how they smell. I love the heft of them in my hands. If I really, really like a book, I've been known to embrace it and pat its cover fondly. That's probably why folks look at me funny when I'm let loose in a bookstore.

In selecting books for gifts, I look for the most delicious ones. I want any book I give to be treasured for years to come, to be so esthetically appealing that the recipient has the same reaction my son did. I'm not talking eye candy, or glossy coffee table show-offs. A gift book is one you want to sink your teeth into, literally and figuratively. Cookbooks, which I give as wedding presents, are the most obvious example. Because I enjoy both reading and cooking, the most luscious cookbooks are not just edible but readable as well. A perfect example is *Frank Stitt's Southern Table*. But try not to lick the pages.

Nature books tend to be especially scrumptious. When I gave the writer Anne Rivers Siddons a copy of Thomas Pakenham's remarkable book, *Meetings with Remarkable Trees*, she held it up to her face and pressed her cheek against it. I've given *Gift from the Sea*, by Anne Morrow Lindbergh, many times but always with a warning: Don't overindulge. It's so rich you should savor only a little bit at the time.

If time is a factor and I don't have the luxury of browsing, sniffing, and feeling my way through the smorgasbord of delectable titles on the shelves, I've found the perfect solution. I give a copy of *Book Lust* by Nancy Pearl. The subtitle is "Recommended Reading for every Mood, Moment, and Reason." I add "Hunger" to the list and wish the recipient *bon appetit*!

MARRIED LOVE
Beth Ann Fennelly

In every book my husband's written, a minor character named Colin suffers a horrible death. This is because my boyfriend before I met my husband was named Colin. In addition to being named Colin, he was Scottish, and an architect. So you understand my husband's feelings of inadequacy. My husband cannot build a tall building of many stories. He can only build *a* story, and then push Colin out of it.

MY WIFE'S GOOD-LOOKING FRIENDS
Tom Franklin

We are at the beach in Indiana, which at first I didn't even know had beaches, and on clear days, across the gray-green lake, you can see a tiny outline of Chicago, as if somebody sketched it in pencil. It's a private beach, like they all are now, fifty yards of prime white sand and a posse of chairs, rafts and umbrellas. It came with the rented house of my wife's good-looking friends, who vacation here each July. Once in a while, like now, on the way from Alabama to visit my wife's other friends in Chicago, we'll stop.

I don't like to visit my wife's good-looking friends because I am average looking. Or less. Everybody says so without quite saying so: *How'd you get her to marry you? You must be rich!* My wife is good-looking herself and fits in among her good-looking friends here on the beach, all of them in bikinis and speedos and with dunes and saw grass and everybody's phone up. But put me in the pictures, and I'm like a beard-ed thug who wandered in from some dark alley. When I offer to take the group shot, everybody smiles brighter.

I prefer my wife's ugly friends. They're from a different period in her life, rehab or grad school. They're the ones in Chicago. They're all fat and their duplex has the AC full blast and there are trays of food everywhere and they never stop eating. The men are balding and red in the face and sometimes the women's feet swell and they can't wear shoes. When we visit I stand outside by the giant grill holding my Bud Light and I feel like the skinniest, best-looking motherfucker in the city, still got all my teeth and a head of fulsome hair stirring in the beefy smoke.

I wonder if my wife's good-looking friends have better-looking friends in some state better than Indiana. Conversely, do my wife's ugly friends in their ugly state have uglier friends yet—think Oklahoma City or Topeka, Kansas, think scars and birth defects, amputations.

By now all the good-looking people have folded their chairs and taken their phones up to the house, and I sit watching the sky darken and the water begin to chop. Then my wife texts that it's time to come in to dinner, they've ordered pizza, from the good place. I gather my IPA beer and damp towel and stand and squint out at where the Chicago skyline used to be. There are plenty of dark alleys in that city where I could disappear, lurking with my thoughts and flaws, my good-looking wife safe across the water with all her good-looking friends.

THE MAN OF THE HOUSE COMES HOME
Michelle Richmond

The coffee is brewed, the dishes done, the house silent, and you are in the zone. Finally, the words are flowing. It's a story you've been meaning to write forever, but somehow you never do. Maybe it will get written today.

And then you hear a door closing—not slamming, just closing with a kind of blunt finality, announcing "I am home." Footsteps pound through the kitchen and into the living room, where you have set up shop on the couch: laptop, coffee, notebook, pen, a blanket over your knees to cut the chill.

The man of the house has come home, and he is on the phone. He sits down in the chair across from you. He is talking in his outside voice. He is making deals, setting meetings, participating in the work of the world.

You pick up your laptop, your coffee cup, your pen, your notebook, and carry everything down the hall to the bedroom. You close the door and set up your makeshift office in bed. You try to return to the zone. It's not easy, reentering the fictional dream after the dream is broken, so you write the first thing that comes to you, a title: "The Man of the House Comes Home."

You begin this story, which is about him but not about him, which is about love and interruption, but mostly interruption. You love him, this man who comes home most days at seven in the evening but today at noon, en route to a different meeting. He is a kind man, a wise man, a man who, like so many men you have known, and possibly every man you have slept with, still quotes *Apocalypse Now* on occasion. It is the ultimate man's movie, these men who have some inkling of the beast within them, but who are by no means beastly. These men who imagine the great escape. These men who are expected to behave heroically (and sometimes do) but who secretly long to be anti-hero instead, loved and lauded for all the wrong reasons.

You love him of course, that is not the issue. But sometimes the space he takes up is bigger than the space you have.

And then he is walking down the hallway, calling your name, and then he is opening the door to the bedroom, a second zone breached, the story ending before it began.

"Hey," he says. "I hope I wasn't too loud."

He wants your intellectual opinion on a matter of some importance involving a meeting that will occur two weeks hence in a country you have never visited, a country known for its meetings among people who dare not meet elsewhere. He does not tell you who he will be meeting, which passport he will be using, under which name. You have never seen most of his passports, you have never called him by most of his names.

"Can I get your thoughts on something?" he asks. You can say that about him: he is always seeking your opinion. He wants to bounce ideas off of you. He wants to know if you agree with his approach, or if you would do it differently.

"Okay, but I'm writing," you say.

"Literature?" he asks, wryly but not unkindly, because it has been so long since you have written fiction, beset as you are by the labors of the home: which is not to say that you cook well or clean well or even take on the majority of the domestic duties, only that you have a teenager, which makes you feel exhausted, incompetent, physically necessary yet existentially unneeded.

"Not exactly," you say.

His curiosity is piqued. He always wants to know what you are writing. He is, after all, your biggest fan, he will always set aside what he is doing to talk about what you are writing, to read it, to praise it, to offer suggestions, most of which are excellent.

"What are you writing then?" he asks, the meeting of great importance momentarily forgotten.

"It's called 'The Man of the House Comes Home'," you say.

He smiles. "I like it." He turns to leave. "I'm sorry. You were working, it can wait."

You close your laptop, slide it off of your lap, turn your focus on him. He is wearing good jeans and a button-down, the uniform of the mature modern male professional in the unwild west. You are wearing sweatpants and a T-shirt he bought you on one of his trips, bearing the name of a city you've never been to, in a country known for its bright blue waters and occasional terroristic bombings. The latest bombing happened in the very hotel he had stayed in, just days after he checked out. You live with the uncomfortable knowledge that his job is not quite safe, that one of his trips might well end in disaster. This may be, after all, why you tolerate his interruptions: you secretly fear any one of them could be the last.

"It's okay. What were you saying?"

He comes to sit on the edge of the bed. A conversation will ensue. This is what you do together. This is marriage. You dislike interruptions, but if you must be interrupted you're glad that he is the one to do it. And without these interruptions, what would get written anyway? You don't really like to leave the house. You are not good at getting out there. He gets out there and participates vividly in the world and brings home this energy, these ideas, these half-stories of events he can never fully reveal, stories comprised of vague impressions and shadows. From these shadows you construct elaborate narratives. For so many years it has been this way.

You will have the conversation and then you will write the story, cannibalizing the life he lives out there for the things you write in here, inside this domestic sphere, on the couch or on the bed or some-times in the kitchen, where you sometimes stand—not to cook but to write, when your back is tired from sitting, when you are waiting for more coffee to brew.

The man of the house is home. In a few minutes he will leave, and you will take up where you left off.

WITH THESE RINGS
Sonny Brewer

I took my navy discharge in Barcelona and hitchhiked to Cadiz. On a northbound train to Madrid, I again unfolded the telegram from my sister. Your father died. And I pulled my seabag from underneath the seat and put both feet on it. I leaned my head against the frosted glass, feeling all over the buzz of the steel wheels on the rails. A week later I flew home. The old man was already in the ground.

His house had been cleaned out. Everybody got what they wanted. Figuring the wayfaring son would be good for some few years traveling light, address unknown, they'd left me out when they divvied up the few things my father left behind. There's a tiny little box, it's wrapped and got your name on it, my sister said.

The sound of my footsteps down the hall toward the back bedroom echoed like the clocking of time toward my own mortgaged future. The last time I'd seen him, he was sitting on the bed, twisting the ruby star sapphire on his right ring finger. Leaning forward, looking at his feet, wiggling his big toe through the ragged hole in his right sock, the Target brand lace-up work shoes paired there on the throw rug. I never could figure you out, you know, he said.

I know, I said.

I came at you too hard, he said.

I made it through okay, I said.

I look at this sapphire ring I got from a street vendor in Saigon and I get back there to the ring. The ring I made you throw out of my car. You must've been eleven or twelve.

I was ten, I said.

It didn't seem right to me, he said, a boy going around with some damn fool notion he had a magic ring. That's some girly shit, I thought, he said.

Yeah, I remember you told me that, I said. I did not say, And you called me a pussy.

It came out of some one-legged bubble gum machine, your mama told me. Plastic with a ruby red setting that had magic power. All for a nickel.

I wondered why she even told you, I said.

Why in the hell not tell me? He asked. It was something to say, at least. News from home, I reckon. Me in that Peterbilt at a Texas truck stop calling your mama before I rolled on out toward Bakersfield. He thinks Linda Parker sat beside him on the school bus, she said, 'cause he wished it so on a ring he got for a nickel—ain't that funny? Pissed me off. Wobbly-ass one-legged gumball machine. Tell him no son of mine needs to be trying to polish a genie out of a ring. Tell him to dig a damn can of worms and get a cane pole and go fishing. Shit. Next thing, he'll be stealing some of your ruffled underwear, I said to your mama.

She told me, I said.

Now that's what don't make no sense, the old man said. Her telling what I said—telling what you did. It was like she was just trying to set us against one another.

Well, the back-and-forth telling got part of the job done, I said.

I know, he said. And the rest of it got done in my Oldsmobile that late afternoon, I expect.

You were taking us all to Columbus to the picture show at the Varsity Theater, I said.

No, it was the Princess, he said. A scary movie. And you kept trying to duck down your head at the good parts.

I dreamed about the good parts for a good long while, I said.

And asked every night could you keep the lamp on in your bedroom.

You didn't let me.

You needed to learn there was nothing in the dark to be scared of. Same kind of imaginary shit as a magic ring is how I saw it. And I stopped in the middle of the highway that day and made you roll down the back window and throw it out of my car. You took it off your finger and dropped it on the seat beside your mama. Like she might pick it up and drop it in her purse and that would suit me, and you'd get it back from her when I got on the road again.

But you threw it back at me, I said. I pitched it toward the barbed wire fence running beside the road. You rolled out to New Jersey, and I walked down the road after school one day and looked for my ring. Didn't get home until dark. Mama was stomping mad. Said I could've been run over on the side of the road. Or kidnapped by a stranger.

None of that happened. And you didn't find that ring, he said, and tucked his thumb into his palm and twisted the ring on his finger.

That's right, I said. And then I was done talking to him and turned to leave his bedroom.

Wait a minute, he said. Will you hear me out? Son?

But I kept walking. I heard him say, Please, son. But I kept going for nine years. And now he's dead. I went into his bedroom to look for the box. My sister said she'd left it on the windowsill. There were no curtains and I saw it right away. It was the size of a matchbox and wrapped with a scrap of notebook paper and the lines were parallel to the box edges. In a tiny script it was addressed to me, just my name, and just his name written upper left like a letter.

The bed was gone, or I would have sat for the unwrapping. Instead, I leaned my shoulder against the wall beside the window. I looked at his handwriting, our names so close together.

I slipped my feet out of my Birkenstocks and eased down to the floor, cross-legged. I held the box in my left hand. The closet door was ajar and his beat-up shoes lay there, one on its side.

I was careful not to tear the paper as I removed the one short strip of cellophane tape from the back. I folded the wrapping and tucked it into my shirt pocket. It was a matchbox and I knew his ring was inside it.

I slid open the box. Another tightly folded piece of the wide-ruled notebook paper lined the bottom and the ruby star sapphire lay on top. I took out the ring and put it on the floor and unfolded the paper.

Son, I finally figured out some things that lifted my hangdog heart. I hope the ring fits and you don't have to have it cut and rewelded. That might mess with its magic.

The ring fit. A little big.

I stood up and walked barefoot to the closet and pulled open the door. I caterpillared my toes into my daddy's right shoe. I rolled the left one upright with my foot and put it on. They were my size.

I walked up the hall. I hoped my sister would come by and see my Birkenstocks. Maybe figure out I'd come for my inheritance. And with my thumb I twisted loose some magic to help me on my travels. I had some things to figure out between now and finally.

WHAT I THINK ABOUT WHEN SOMEONE USES "PUSSY" AS A SYNONYM FOR "WEAK"

Beth Ann Fennelly

At the deepest part of the deepest part, I rocked shut like a stone. I'd climbed as far inside me as I could. Everything else had fallen away. Midwife, husband, bedroom, world: quaint concepts. My eyes were clamshells. My ears were clapped shut by the palms of the dead. My throat was stoppered with bees. I was the fox caught in the trap, and I was the trap. Chewing off a leg would have been easier than what I now required of myself. I understood I was alone in it. I understood I would come back from there with the baby, or I wouldn't come back at all. I was beyond the ministrations of loved ones. I was beyond the grasp of men. Even their prayers couldn't penetrate me. The pain was such that I made peace with that. I did not fear death. Fear was an emotion, and pain had scalded away all emotions. I chose. In order to come back with the baby, I had to tear it out at the root. Understand, I did this without the aid of my hands.

WHO IS THE REAL PIG BOY?
From *PIG BOY'S WICKED BIRD*
Doug Crandell

The adults around the boy didn't understand his weight gain; they couldn't figure out how the toddler had put on extra pounds when he hadn't been eating. He appeared to be bulging under his pleated shorts, his tummy full and plump. He was a farm child and at first the grownups thought he might have the worms, what with the way his belly arched, but they quickly determined this was not the case. He was extremely healthy in every regard: bright eyes, hair luminous, stomach not merely distended with air but pudgy, like a working man's. Yet the boy hadn't been eating lately. He wouldn't touch the sausage and corn pones at breakfast, or the ham and eggs at lunch, or the flavorful evening meal of stew, beans, more cornbread, and slices of thick cheese. They were perplexed: how was the child becoming fuller and fuller, skin smooth and perfect, his little hands chubby and nails pink, with fine half-moons of white near the quick?

One day, after the men and older boys had gone to the fields, the grandmother (or was it the mother? an aunt? or perhaps a female friend of the family?) decided to follow the little guy wherever he went. It was a family farm, and not much thought was given to allowing a child to roam around unattended to explore the pasture or play in the corn. Most of the adults simply thought it safe for children to be children and let the young ones play until they got hungry and came looking for food. But this boy had not been coming back to the house for his meals. The woman was determined to find out why.

At first, the little boy merely sat in the tall grass of the pasture, where he played with butterflies and plucked grass to chew. The woman watched him from behind a tree. She knew the grass could not be putting on the little boy's pounds and certainly wouldn't keep him from eating at regular meals. Before long the child became bored and got to his feet. He waddled down a worn hog path to the side entrance of the farrowing house. The spring had been plentiful in terms of newborn piglets; the building held more than ten litters. The sows were all sea-soned matrons; they were well mannered and docile, good mothers and even better livestock.

The woman watched through the door of the shed as the little boy strode down the aisle where the sows lay on their sides, grunting, urging their piglets to quit running around in chase and come to nurse. The woman closed her eyes for a minute, trying to keep herself from thinking of what she knew she'd see when she opened them.

The boy struggled over a plank separating the stall from the aisle. He managed to pull his weight over the partition; the woman thought for sure that she heard his tight little shorts rip. She opened her eyes. The fat baby boy was down on his round belly suckling from a crossbred sow. The other little pigs, his siblings, squealed to get him to move over so that they might find a teat; the sow perked her ears at this commotion but remained flat on her side, underbelly splayed wide so that her young could easily nurse.

The little boy seemed to doze off as he drank from the sow's nipple. The woman was shocked but oddly relieved. The boy would have to be stopped, of course, but at least he didn't have some dreadful disease that made him look healthy while inside he invisibly starved to death. On the farm, only cow's milk was used for human beings, and the woman knew, from bottle feeding piglets that had lost their moth-ers during birthing, that sow's milk was bitter, almost sour tasting. She wondered how on earth the child had ever gotten used to the taste, but instantly, seeing the boy nursing, she could understand how he might've thought this was simply natural. After all, there were more pigs around him than humans, and both he and the piglets were roughly in the same developmental stage, so it made sense to her that the little boy thought what he was doing was normal, even proper and right.

The woman waited until the little boy had fallen completely asleep. She opened the shed door quietly and walked to the stall where he lay deeply dreaming. She had to position herself just right, maneu-vering over the partition to lift the heavy child from the pile of piglets that had crowded around him for warmth. The woman struggled to pull the full child to her bosom and strained to cradle his bulk as she toted him to the house. Once she got him inside, and he woke up, she would tell him how he was not to do what he'd been doing, how it wasn't clean and that God made mommy sows for baby pigs and regular mommies for baby boys and girls. But for now she'd let him sleep, his blond, sweaty bangs clinging to his forehead, the scent of sharp milk on his hot breath as he breathed in and out like a little piglet.

CHITLINS
Robert St. John

I once wrote a semi-controversial column about eating possum. I was unexpectedly bombarded with phone calls and emails from proud and angry possum eaters. I had never eaten possum. I still haven't eaten possum. I began to worry that there were other controversial Southern delicacies that I'd been missing out on.

I'd never eaten chitlins, either. Chitlins are a very divisive food. You're either a chitlin lover or a chitlin hater. Actually, you're "on the fence" until you eat your first bite, and then you quickly hop on one side or the other. I wondered about all of the fuss. Being the acutely intuitive investigative food journalist that I am, I decided to delve further.

I hesitated to write about chitlins after the possum incident; for fear that some readers might think my column had moved in a different direction, and that my eating habits had headed down into the deep, dark, endless depths of the culinary root cellar. Some might say I was already in the cellar, and an in-depth treatise on the glory and wonder of the almighty chitlin was an improvement.

The official name for chitlins is "chitterlings," but I don't use that spelling since no one pronounces it that way. It's silly. It's sort of like insisting on the correct "opossum" for what everybody calls a "possum." Nobody does it, and I won't start here.

Chitlins are pig intestines. And we all know what runs through intestines. Needless to say, chitlins must be thoroughly cleaned. My friend Banks Norman eats chitlins. He has tried to talk me into eating them. Last week, he told me how they were cleaned: he slings them against a tree stump, runs a hose through them, picks off the fat, and boils them for four hours, draining and changing the water three times during the boiling process, while skimming and picking more fat. (Banks says the slinging is the best part. He's a pro. He's been slinging the same stuff verbally for years, long before he cleaned his first chitlin.)

Four hours? Slinging intestines against a stump? Having to drain a boiled ingredient three times before frying it? Chitlins must be extremely tasty to go to all of that trouble.

Banks is a kidder. He keeps a few spare kernels of corn in his shirt pocket while eating chitlins. When no one is looking, he will slip the kernels into his mouth and wait for the perfect moment during the meal to spit them out into his hand. "Hey! Who cleaned these chitlins?"

Never having eaten pig intestines, I imagined they would have the consistency of crispy-fried calamari with the flavor of smoked bacon—a slightly rubbery texture with a nice hint of piquant pork surrounded by a crispy-fried breading of seasoned French bread crumbs. Sounds good to me. I have eaten bacon-wrapped Diver scallops, Oysters en Brochette, shrimp wrapped in bacon, and broiled oysters stuffed with bacon dressing. The seafood-pork pairing is well known. Maybe chitlins—and this imagined calamari/pork combination—would taste like those familiar dishes.

Andouille sausage is made from chitlins and tripe. I love Andouille sausage.

One of my favorite catfish houses is Rayner's Seafood House. The Rayners have been frying fish in the same location on US 49 north of Hattiesburg since 1961. Rayner's is home to some of the best fried catfish in Mississippi. They serve fried green tomatoes, fried dill pickles, excellent coleslaw, and some of the best hushpuppies you will find.

While eating catfish at Rayner's, I noticed a sign that read:

Chitlins Tuesday Only
Fried or boiled—all you can eat $12.95
Half & Half—all you can eat $14.95
Dasani Water $1.00

At first I wondered if anyone ever took full advantage of the all-you-can-eat promise. I can't imagine anyone consuming more than one plate of chitlins. I also wondered what bottled water had to do with eating chitlins. Those two foodstuffs seemed diametrically opposed. As an uneducated chitlin eater, I wondered if bottled water was required to eat chitlins. I began to worry. Does bottled water make them cleaner? Does bottled water make them taste better? Does it have something to do with the cleaning process that I don't know about? Is there something in chlorinated tap water that interacts with pig intestines and makes you grow hairy ears, a snout, and tusks? Note to self: When eating chitlins, order bottled water.

And why is the combo platter two dollars more? I have a theory, but we will get to boiled chitlins later.

I decided to return to Rayner's on the following Tuesday and boldly go where no St. John had gone before—into the culinary root cellar that is the underbelly of the pig . . . chitlins!

Chitlin night at Rayner's is busy.

I ordered an all-you-can-eat fried chitlins and a glass of sweet tea.

Sensing that I was a virgin chitlin eater, Kim Rayner asked if I wanted them "fried crispy." Sensing Kim was a veteran chitlin server, I replied, "Most definitely so." I also ordered a small sampling of boiled chitlins (just to see what they looked like) and an order of fried shrimp (every good businessman has a contingency plan).

In short order, Kim Rayner delivered my plate of chitlins. "How do you eat them?" I asked.

"Oh, I don't eat them. But you'll be fine, just use a lot of hot sauce."

I should've known right then that something smelled fishy. Well, not actually fishy.

Sitting there on the plate, chitlins looked like any number of fried foods. But there was a smell. I can't quite identify the smell, but I can report that I have never smelled anything quite like it. It is a distinct smell. Make that a distinct funk.

The funk drifted up from the plate, surrounded my face and dug into my nostrils, where it kidnapped each individual pore of both sinus passages for the next twelve hours. I went home and changed clothes, still smelled it. I washed my face, still there. I jumped in the shower—lathered, rinsed, and repeated—still there. I had to snort two bottles of Neo-Synephrine to deliver me from that chitlinized trip to nasal hell.

Gathering up all the epicurean courage I could muster, I took a bite. Actually, I only ate a small piece off of one individual chitlin. Singular: chitli.

Friends and neighbors, chitlins don't taste anything like calamari. I used hot sauce and ketchup on my chitli and it still didn't taste good. To me, chitlins taste like they smell. Hot sauce doesn't help.

I glanced over at the bowl of boiled chitlins. I don't know what I expected boiled chitlins to look like, maybe Faith Hill's legs or the seat of Jennifer Lopez's jeans. No such luck. Boiled chitlins look like . . . well, like . . . boiled intestines! I resorted to the backup plan and ate my fried shrimp.

I'm sure Mickey Rayner cooks world-class chitlins. The restaurant was crowded, so, as chitlins go, I'm sure his are outstanding. I found out from his wife, Kim, that Mickey is not a chitlin eater, either (every good businessman gives the people what they want).

There were a couple of sweet little ladies at a table near me. Each of them had finished off a large plate of chitlins. One of them told me to take the chitlins home and "reheat them for two minutes in the microwave."

Thanks, I'll pass.

Then the night began to turn ugly. Other customers began chiming in. One lady said she cooked them in "celery, onions, lemons, salt, pepper, and carrots."

"Doesn't that smell bad?"

"I boil them outside, baby,"

"Yes, but doesn't that smell bad outside?"

"When it's hot, you don't cook them. Fresh pork makes your blood pressure go up."

Frozen pork makes your blood pressure go up, too, lady.

Another nearby customer said, "There are as many ways to cook chitlins as there are cooks that cook chitlins."

Yes, sir, There are also as many ways to torture small animals as there are small animals, but you don't see me doing it.

Banks boils chitlins in crab boil. When I complained to him about how my chitli tasted, he said, "Mine taste like crab boil."

"Why not just eat crabs or shrimp?" I asked.

He looked puzzled for a minute and then said, "I don't know."

I am not a food snob. But, if it means I will be labeled a food snob if I never eat chitlins again, then I will proudly wear that moniker like a gastronomic badge of honor.

44

Before the chitlin research project I was asking myself how I could've lived in the Piney Woods of South Mississippi for forty-one years and not eaten chitlins. Now I know. Maybe I'll let forty-one more years pass and try them again. The year will be 2044 and I'll visit the next generation of Rayner's, and eat more than one chitli. Then again, maybe I'll have my usual catfish and shrimp. An eighty-two year-old heart can't take that much stress.

WHEN GRAVITY LETS GO
Marlin Barton

For the better part of two hours, as you've sat at his bedside, your father has made perfect sense, each complaint reasonable enough, though tiring, as always—another old man unhappy with the world, with his life, with the psychiatric floor of this hospital that smells of bleach and worse. He's made no mention of the millions denied him, even when he answered every written request, hundreds of them, for the twenty-dollar processing fee. No mention of his mother, your grandmother, who lived until one hundred and four and then began to visit him because he asked God to allow it, and God kept allowing it, would not let her stop, or make her stop, despite her ugly tone and the way she would disappear before she'd answer your father's questions. "Maybe God is punishing you for something you shouldn't have asked for," you told him and knew you shouldn't have.

"He's found me here," your father says now. "I don't know how. The son of a bitch."

You've dreaded this. By *he* your father means, as you well know, the man who lived down the hall in the old apartment building and began to break into your father's rooms and move his things around. This was after someone kidnapped your dead grandmother and you had to take your father's pistols away, the ones he wasn't supposed to have, but the apartment manager said as long as you took them, he could stay. But when he grabbed the arm of the man down the hall, spun him around, and told him not to break into his apartment again or he'd kill him, the lack of pistols wasn't enough. Your father is still strong, powerful. People can sense it, including the nurses here who care for him.

"How do you know he's been here?" you ask. "Have you seen him?"

"He left his mark. See?" he says and points at a triangular scratch on the wall near his bed.

When you try to dismiss the notion that the man could show

up here, all you do is show your father, once again, how foolish you can be. He acknowledges it with one dismissive, disgusted turn of his head. And you want to punch him in the face, but you are not as strong as him and you both know it, though he has never laid a hand on you and could not even bear to spank you as a child.

"The man is a psychopath. He's crazy. I don't know why he picked me."

You nod and say no more. Finally, you get up from your chair, take his hand in yours, and tell him you'll see him again in a few days. You are tired from sitting, but you help pull him up from the bed, feel his strong grip on your hand, and you hug him and say good-bye.

Once outside, you glance back at the four floors of the hospital building and think of the line a poet once wrote, "I have just come down from my father," but unlike in the poem, you do not search the hospital windows for your father's room, and your father isn't dying. He is merely unmoored, on his way to being lost, but has not found his way there yet, not completely. Maybe the medication the doctors started giving him will help. They can keep him two more weeks. Then, if he is better, maybe he can go back to the small apartment you found for him after he had to leave the old one. And if he's not better (and you know he won't be), what then? You don't know. You are at your wits end. But where is that end exactly?

This is not a town you know well, though once you are out of the parking lot and turn down the residential street and make one more left, you are soon on the right highway, but you didn't turn south toward home. Maybe you are looking for a place to eat. This is your third trip here. You guess there are places on this road, maybe a diner that serves food like your grandmother used to cook, the grandmother who returned to the living and would not leave.

The one thing you do know about this town named with strange syllables from a Native American tongue is that it's the only place in the world where a meteorite fell from the heavens, tore through a roof, and hit a woman on her hip as she lay on her sofa, maybe while listening to a radio which would soon carry her strange news to the world. On your second trip, you saw the marker beside the road that commemorates the site, the house no longer standing, an empty field in its place.

You drive, drive farther, and still see no place to eat. Finally, you decide to turn around and pull onto a narrow, unlined blacktop, but someone is directly behind you, and so you keep going and then turn left onto another narrow road that you think might carry you back to the highway. You notice the sign that says Gravity Hill Lane and the name strikes you as odd. The beat-up blue four-door behind turns with you and then passes. It is full of teenagers. You hear their music blaring. You follow, remember yourself as a teenager, and think of your father as he was in those years—solid, taking on the weight of you, his son. Up ahead you see a stop sign and the highway beyond it. But the carload of teenagers stops well before the sign in a low place in the road, a dip in the blacktop. A teenage boy looks out the back window and begins to laugh. A blond-haired girl beside him does the same. You wonder what is funny. You? Then the car begins to roll up the incline, toward you, and all in the car are turning their heads this way and that, laughing harder, shrugging their shoulders, as if what is happening can't be believed. They are not trying to back into you. You feel no threat, but you back up and give them room, and they keep rolling uphill. Then they finally come to a stop, and wait, as if some explanation will occur to them in a few moments. The girl and boy now smile at you, gently wave good-bye, and the car accelerates forward. It merely slows at the stop sign and turns onto the highway.

You ease ahead, into the dip, and stop, wanting to experience whatever it was that filled them with such rising, lifting joy. For a moment you are unsure what to do. Then you slowly pull the gearshift into reverse, but you do not take your foot off the brake, not yet. Something else is needed here, some letting go of logic, of sound reason. You place your car in neutral and slowly lift your foot from the brake. You wait a moment and then feel logic letting go, the gravity that pulled a meteorite toward this town, this place on earth, no longer at work. You are rolling up an incline. It is a fact. This is no illusion created by anyone, no optical illusion either, and certainly not a delusion on your part. You aren't the one deluded. You are laughing, not waiting for an explanation, and then you are laughing harder. You wish your father were sitting beside you, some younger version of himself, at the age you are now maybe, laughing with you, everything incomprehensible in your lives making perfect sense to the both of you.

KENTUCKY-CAROLINA
Lynn Pruett

Lila and Dwight Lesperance sat at the edge of the couch. On the TV screen, the Kentucky Wildcats played an intense game of basketball against the North Carolina Tar Heels. Ice rattled in Lila's drink. A fire burned in the wood stove. The game was close.

Lila was glad for the distraction of the game. She had an appointment she had not told Dwight about because the last thing she wanted was to become a bed-ridden patient with him as the ever-watchful caregiver. He'd monitor every action of her body from its feeding to its voiding and record the awkward details in a notebook, testing her schedule against what the medical print-out said it should be. Dwight had tried to keep their oldest son, Rob, on a feeding schedule when the boy was a newborn. The result was a red-faced starving infant who tore Lila's nipples when she came home from work to nurse him.

There was a loud crash from upstairs.

Lila sipped her whiskey. Dwight pounded the coffee table and shouted at the Tar Heel taking a foul shot, "Your shoe's untied!" As pointless here in the living room as it was when he shouted it from their nosebleed seats in the stands. The game was in its final minute and the score was tied.

Their middle son, Trevor, ambled into the room. He was fifteen, thin and philosophical. "Hey, Dad, you know that vase on your dresser?"

Lila stifled a laugh while Dwight froze.

"I kinda knocked it off." He stood between the couch and the screen.

There were seventeen seconds left in the game. Neither Lila nor Dwight moved. "Your grandfather was in there," Dwight said.

"Whoa," Trevor said. "It's not very much gunk for such a big guy."

Dwight waved his arm to clear Trevor from his view.

"Right. The game." Trevor bowed from the waist and backed

50

out of the room.

When the game ended in a Wildcat victory, Dwight went upstairs and Lila went into the kitchen and made supper for herself, Trevor, and Rocky, their youngest son. Dwight had to attend a film student's screening, offer a critique, and then bolster the student's dashed ego by forcing him to have dinner with the very committee that had shredded his work.

After dinner, Lila climbed the stairs to the bedroom. She startled at the threshold. From the dresser, ashes jetted out in a fan on the floor toward the bed. Shards of the vase, sullied by gray powder, sparkled with malicious intent. In the months to come, they could cut Dwight's soft white feet or her own. How absolutely perfect that from the grave the creepy old man had managed to get himself flung across her bedroom floor. He had sent them a new VCR and a porn film of his favorite scenes for a wedding present.

She phoned Dwight, who was at dinner, and apparently eager to jump up and leave the table. When he was outside the restaurant, she asked. "Is there anything you want me to do with the ashes?"

"I already got what I wanted." He coughed. "There were bone fragments."

"You don't want the rest?"

"No," he gushed, deep and primordial and rare.

Lila went to the basement and lugged the shop vac upstairs. She turned it on high and happily watched it suck up the remains of Bob Wye. When the floor was clean and gleaming, all gold pinewood, she took the shop vac downstairs, removed the bag, tied it with a tidy twist tie, and dropped it in the trash. There was great pleasure in this action. She almost wept. What a gift from Dwight, this duty, which was no duty, but an experience of tremendous joy.

SLACABAMORINICO
Michelle Richmond

The Sunday before Fat Tuesday in the port city of Mobile, revelers dance on Joe Cain's grave in the Church Street Cemetery. In 1866, Joe Cain rode through the streets of Mobile on the back of a coal wagon, dressed as Slacabamorinico, the legendary Chickasaw chief. Joe Cain and his crew made a general ruckus. An old mule plodded along before them. "Take this," Joe said to the Union troops who occupied the city.

Those who dance on Joe Cain's grave are quick to tell you it all started here, in the streets of Mobile in eighteen and sixty-six. They christen the headstone with beer bottles, water the grass around his grave with straight bourbon and piss. Men dress in women's clothing. Women stand on shifting balconies of old French hotels, lift their shirts for passing floats, bare their breasts to the kindly spirit of Joe Cain. Joe Cain's bones dance a knock-kneed lay-down kind of dance at the sight of the bare-chested happy women. On Joe Cain's grave, teenage boys get laid for the first time, and the heat of their quick love seeps down into the fertile earth. Slacabamorinico is rumored to be buried somewhere on the outskirts of Mobile County, in an unmarked grave near an abandoned skating rink.

The year before Hurricane Frederic, our father took Darlene and Celia and me to the Crewe of Columbus parade. We clambered to catch plastic necklaces and chocolate doubloons, felt the crowd crushing forward as we sang the Moon Pie chant. A big man in overalls nearly knocked me over when he reached out to catch a shower of Jolly Ranchers. He stepped on my foot and sloshed beer on my shirt. On the way home I ate twenty-six Now & Laters and vomited out the window of our Galaxie 500.

When we got home our mother was waiting at the front door. "You smell like beer!" she said, dragging me inside. I felt grown up and slightly sinful, like the prodigal child come home. My mother was so angry she locked my father out of the house. Late into the evening he paid penance for the debauchery we had witnessed, sitting on the doorstep staring out at the street.

Years later I would learn of the infamous Cowbellions, with their rakes and hoes and cowbells, their bovine inclinations, their triumphant march through the streets of Mobile decades before the war. Drunk on whiskey and New Year, they rang their bells and clanged their rakes until the whole city awoke. In their hearts that night there was no inkling of the coming War of Northern Aggression, no thought of the slaves who peered in disbelief from the dim windows of their shanties. Mobilians don't know that the party has long since ended, clinging hardheadedly to the notion that the Confederates won the war.

MARY AND THE SCHOOLBOY
A lost chapter from *The Hidden Light of Northern Fires*
Daren Wang

Mary Willis had just seen her father and her brother Leander off and was finishing the breakfast dishes when a sharp banging at the door sent the kitchen girl scurrying up the back stairs to the safety of her room.

The man on the front porch wore his blonde hair oiled, his mustache waxed, and his muskrat overcoat unbuttoned to show his pressed suit. The turn of his lips made clear that he was pleased with himself for duping Leander with his story. Mary could see that he'd left his sidearm hanging on the horse's saddle to avoid wrinkling his suit.

The horse, she had to admit, was a beautiful animal with a perfect gray coat that shimmered in the sun.

"What can I do for you?" she asked, wiping her hands on her apron.

"I'm Shelby Bell," he said in the lazy drawl of Virginia. He smiled back at her. "I've tracked my slave up from Harpers Ferry, and I have reason to believe he might be on your farm."

Mary leaned into the door frame, dropping her arm out of his sight.

He was about Leander's age, a few years younger than her. She took in his self-satisfied grin and his ridiculous suit and wondered why she'd spent so much time fretting over him. He wasn't short, but she was a tall woman, and stood an inch over him. She could imagine other women finding him handsome, but he exuded privilege in a way that made her want to slap him. She told herself she would not allow herself to be afraid of him again.

"Why, it's illegal to house runaways, isn't it?" Mary asked. "Are you implying that I would do such a thing?"

"No, not you, of course but still some do," Bell said. "I'm sure a lady like you wouldn't involve yourself in anything so unseemly, but his tracks end on the farm. He could be hiding in your chicken coop and you wouldn't even know it. He's quite dangerous, you know. Why don't you let me search the farm, and take him away? He just about killed me with a rock when he escaped," he said. "And then he laid up another man with his bare hands just a couple nights ago in the woods not far from here."

"I heard about that at the quilting bee yesterday," Mary lied. "The poor soul. Is he going to be alright?"

"Mr. Dratch seems like a resilient man, but it'd be best for everyone to remove my slave from his reach before he gets back on his feet," Bell said. "Shall I take a look?"

"My father's away right now, and I don't think he would like it if I were to let you search without him here," Mary said.

The southerner frowned.

"Can I wait for him?" he asked.

"I simply couldn't have such a handsome gentlemen caller without a chaperone," she said. "I only entertain guests with proper supervision."

He shifted on his feet and kicked at a clump of snow.

"Why don't you let me search and if I find the fugitive, no one needs to know anything about it?" he said, his voice reasonable and sweet. "But if I have to go and get a federal marshal to search your house, then there certainly will be prison and a fine for harboring a slave. It would be a disgrace for a lady such as yourself and her family to go through that."

Her hand rested on the wall, inches from where she kept her pistol hanging from a peg.

"Did you wait until my father and brother rode away before coming to the house?" she asked.

The same toothy smile stayed on his face, but his brow furrowed.

"Excuse me?" he said.

"You heard me," she said. "Did you wait for my father and brother to leave so that you could come over here and deal with little old me instead of two strong men?"

He looked past her shoulder into the parlor.

"There's no one else you can talk with," she said, seeing the glance. "It's just me, the lady of the house, as you had hoped for."

"I, um . . ." he faltered, searching for a way to restart his re-hearsed conversation. Finally, he plowed ahead "I'm here to search this farm for my slave. I've ridden up from Harpers Ferry."

"Harpers Ferry? Where they hanged John Brown?" she asked. "Imagine some slave wanting to run away from there."

Bell's face grew cloudy.

"I saw that madman hang," he sneered. "I remember the way he kicked as he swung—"

"I'm sure that's a moment you'll take to your grave," she said, cutting him off. "Aren't you and your fellow slavers calling for secession from the Union?"

"That's right. We will not live under this tyrant Lincoln," Bell said, and Mary thought he puffed his chest out a bit as he spoke.

"So as a secessionist, what claim do you have here on Ameri-can soil?" she asked. "What gives you the right to be here?"

The furrows returned to Bell's forehead.

She knew she should just keep quiet and shut the door, but in this pompous pretty boy, she had found the target for her political frustrations.

"Let's not make this a personal thing," he said. "The constitu-tion obliges you to turn over any slaves you might be harboring. It's a matter of states' rights."

"But it *is* personal," Mary said, looking the man in the eye. "You stand on my front porch and demand to search my farm? What about New York's states' rights? Why should I let a man from a foreign land search this farm? Perhaps we should just secede ourselves, our own little farm here. How about you? Would you let a Celestial just barge in and search your little slave camp down in Virginia?"

"It's no camp. It's the largest plantation in Harper's Ferry," Bell said, then stared at her silently for a moment before setting his jaw. "I don't care about what New York state thinks is legal. I'll search the property with or without your blessing."

He turned his back to her and started to step off the porch.

"So states' rights don't matter, after all, I see," she asked his back, trying to keep him away from his weapon. "Y'all only care about having some poor black man to pick your cotton."

She drew the y'all out deliberately long.

He turned and blinked at her as the color rose in his face.

"I've had enough of this diddly shit," he said, his voice little more than a whisper. "I know he's wounded and laid up here somewhere. Just give me my nigger."

"You should know better than to use a word like that around a lady," Mary said, smiling sweetly as she brought the pistol around and laid it across the white lace bib of her house dress.

It took a moment for him to recognize what he was looking at.

"What kind of lady greets visitors with a Remington?" he asked, his face flushing with anger.

"A frightened one," Mary answered, batting her eyes. "And this, sir, is a Colt Pocket Pistol. Mr. Remington's pistol drifts to the right far too much for me."

"Is this what they teach you Northern whores?" he muttered, stepping backward.

"Oh my," she said, fanning herself with her free hand, before leveling the pistol at him and cocking the gun. "I'm sure it would forever besmirch your family's name if you were to be shot dead by a Yankee woman protecting her honor. I suggest you leave."

He splayed his hands in a motion somewhere between warding and surrender.

"Just stay calm," he said.

She pulled the trigger and the lead ball passed inches from his head and splintered a jagged hole in the trunk of the cherry tree behind him. The horse, just a few feet away, bucked on its tether.

Bell yelped and stumbled backward, falling into the muddy snow.

"I *am* calm," she smiled. "You're the one screeching like a little schoolboy. Now get on your fancy horse and leave."

The Virginian climbed to his feet, and eyed his own pistol, but he could see that hers was leveled at him.

"This isn't over," he said as he mounted the horse. "You'll burn for this."

SILENCE
Patricia Foster

It's March 13, 1965, a Saturday night. My sister and I are "doing hair" for friends who lounge on the soft comforters of our twin beds or sit cross-legged on the floor in slips and flip-flops as we get ready for a party at the VFW club, our party clothes hanging from the closet doors. Tonight, there are only five of us, Jean rolling Linda's dark shoulder-length hair on orange juice cans while Joan sits under the beauty-shop-style "hood" dryer my mother bought for us last year. Judy calls out "talk *louder*" from the bathroom where she's shaving her legs. Because it's Saturday night, we're giddy with anticipation as if we might slip through the world of contradictions, escape the ordinary and be touched by divinity. We breathe in the coming night's happiness as if inside a dream: we know the Elberta boys will be there, tall, lanky boys, already tan and beautiful with unforgivably long lashes framing pale green eyes. They're farmers' sons. They drive their daddy's chicken trucks to and from dances, getting out in a feverish pack as if they have so much energy they absolutely *must* jostle and smack each other before ambling into those damp, crowded rooms. Already, I can see them standing together by the refreshment table at the VFW Club sipping Pepsi and 7-Up from paper cups, then squeezing those cups into tight-wadded shards to torpedo each other.

As we flip through the pages of *Mademoiselle* or stare at the glitter of our newly painted nails, we believe that everything lies ahead of us. *Everything.* Not just tonight's party but awards, books, proms, concerts, recitals, and college followed by what we call "the rest of our lives."

Our lives. As we stand before the mirror primping, smoothing "Pretty-As-Pink" lipstick on our lips and sweeping a tiny brush of dark mascara through our eyelashes, we never think of our lives as a cloister of whiteness, a code of conformity. But it's exactly that: we're white girls with white girlfriends, boyfriends, teachers, mentors, preachers, doctors, coaches, neighbors, ballgames, and parties. The only Black people we know are the maids who come into our houses once a week to mop the kitchen floor and iron our fathers' shirts and the Black men who mow our lawns or work as janitors at the public school. And yet, even as we curl and spray our hair, the Civil Rights Movement is blazing through the once slumbering cities and towns of Alabama, marchers and activists demanding racial justice, planning sit-ins, teach-ins, giving speeches, registering voters, and even going to jail. Though the violence against them is brutal and televised, its reality doesn't penetrate our lives as if we're enveloped in a fog of whiteness, a hush of silence, a cocoon of ignorance.

Tonight, as we gossip about the Elberta boys, wondering who'll be first to break from the pack and ask one of us to dance, no one mentions the six hundred peaceful marchers who crossed the Edmund Pettus Bridge in Selma last Sunday only to be met by a wall of state troopers, mounted deputies, and white spectators waving Confederate flags. No one mutters, "My god, did you *see* how horrible it was . ." how the troopers, their faces disguised by gas masks, rushed the crowd, striking men, women, and children with "sticks, clubs, whips and rubber tubing wrapped in barbed wire" to the riotous cheering of bystanders. In truth, no one has said a word all week about "Bloody Sunday," not at the dinner table, in the classroom, or from the pulpit as if we aren't living in Alabama, but in a place where goodness and mercy shine down and all we need worry about is who we'll become, never once questioning how that becoming might restrict or violate others' lives.

"Come on." My sister nudges me as Joan waits patiently before the full-length mirror. "You do the back while I do the front and sides."

When I glance at Joan, her sudden beauty takes me by surprise: the soft curve of her cheek, the arched brows, the tumble of her chestnut hair as I unwind the rollers and stack them on the dresser. Not once do I think of her as white, privileged, and part of our silence. Not once do I think, *she can go to the public library and read anything she wants.* Instead, I begin combing out her hair, the strands luscious and thick, the ends loosely curled, smooth and lovely, their golden hue shimmering in the evening light. She will be chosen. I know it.

TEACH ME
David Wright Faladé

"Teach me," a friend said to me last week. "You're a university professor. I want to know what I need to do to make things better for you."

It's now a month after the death of Houstonian George Floyd, and my friend asked me to lunch in reaction to the ongoing Black Lives Matter protests that have arisen since. I'll confess: her request threw me. She and I are both fifty-something Texans, both from the Panhandle — me, Borger; her, from a small town near Tulia, with its wretched history of racism by their local criminal justice system. She is white and dear to me; we dated for a time. I'm black.

"What is it you want me to teach you?" I started, then heard myself following with: "Why is it I have to teach you things you should already know?"

My sisters playfully chide me for being the stereotypical "angry black man" —Malcolm Farrakhan, one calls me—but I wasn't trying to hurt my friend's feelings. I genuinely wanted—and want—to understand. Given that the idea of race and racial difference is constructed—I'm not born with a gene that makes me a better dancer or more drawn to watermelon—then the fact that the police aim their policing disproportionately more at me than her is a by-product of how they've been conditioned by society and sanctioned by policies to see me as more of a threat. Yet, while it's me who directly suffers from racism and therefore might seem to be the one to benefit from it ending, the problem is still hers at least as much as it is mine. She doesn't seem to recognize this.

Racism in the United States is an American problem. Unlike most others, our country was built on a set of ideals—about the right to life, liberty and the pursuit of happiness. While shortfalls and outright failure in achieving these aims directly harm some, it's to the detriment of all. And not merely in an abstract, heaven-or-hell moral way, but in the here and now. When I feel my children are at risk, I'll do whatever I have to, to deal with the threat.

But when it's your son who, on only his third shift on the force, is ordered by his training officer to put his body weight on the back of a prone man while the supervisor kneels on the man's neck, this makes of your son a murderer, and so it harms you and your entire family. When, in order to deter future migrants, your niece who works at the Border Patrol Processing Center in McAllen is ordered to take a baby from the arms of the Honduran mother breastfeeding him and handcuff and remove the mother, this makes of your niece a torturer, and so it harms you and your entire family. If we, as a society, stop attempting to live up to our national ideals, then the experiment of American freedom, however flawed, has failed, and all of us, the entire country, suffer for it.

Another piece of our shared problem is that white people, even well-meaning ones like my friend, tend to disbelieve black people when we tell them our realities. They want to believe, but it's hard for them to. When I say that the store clerk seems to be following me or that the attendant spoke to me disrespectfully, my friend tends to see it as an anomaly. The impulse is to reduce the American experience to a single experience—white people's—and the troubling event becomes the result of "one bad apple," not of institutions and systems that cause these people to treat me in this way.

Was the travesty of the killing of twelve-year-old Tamir Rice, shot while playing in a city park by an officer who'd already been fired by one police department before being hired by Cleveland's, just a one-off? The answer, of course, is no. Because George Floyd in Minneapolis, and because Breonna Taylor in Louisville, and because Elijah McClain in Aurora, because, because, because…

African Americans and other people of color are the obvious victims. But all Americans are victimized because the promise of "America" dies a little more with each new death.

It was one hundred and sixty-eight years ago that Frederick Douglass delivered his speech, "What to the Slave is the Fourth of July?" More than just calling for the abolition of slavery, he also spoke of a grander mission still—that the society of his day strive to finally achieve the ideals of equality for all Americans. How is it that, a century and a half later, and after a bloody civil war, after another one hundred years of struggle for civil rights and so many martyrs gone, we still, today, read Douglass's speech with contemporary relevance and not merely as an historical document?

How is it that white people don't know any more than they know?

How is it that I, a professor who attempts to teach your children these fundamental truths, have to also teach them to you?

TWO SISTERS, ONE THINNER,
ONE BETTER DRESSED
Beth Ann Fennelly

When my sister and I would meet at her apartment before heading out to bars, I would choose my clothes with care. I knew that when I walked through her door, she would study me, especially if a few weeks or more had passed since we'd seen each other. Sisters are envious, sure, but we were also information gathering. We looked a bit alike, so it was a way to test how we'd fare in a different outfit, haircut. She was often thinner than I was, but I had better style. Younger by two years, I was her leader only in fashion; I would often be wearing something she hadn't yet considered. She would ask me where I got it, and I would tell her, maybe showing off a little. Sometimes she'd want to try it on and I would accessorize her, cuff her jeans or angle the belt correctly on her hips. If she asked, we'd swap outfits for the night. It was worth being the frumpier one to make her happy.

I'm still aware of how I look when I visit her. I live in a different state now, so it's not as often, but when I'm back in Illinois at our mom's house, I always end my run by visiting her. I stand panting in the grass at my sister's feet. I'm aware of how she sees me, huffing clouds from my lungs, my legs strong, my skin bright with sweat in my new running clothes. Still showing off, I suppose, as she's stuck wearing the navy suit I chose the last time I styled her, a suit now thirteen years outdated, though fashionable enough when they closed the casket.

RELATED SEARCHES
Beth Ann Fennelly

When you search for a term in Google, the results page suggests other commonly-used search terms.

For example, if you type in my name, related searches include:

Beth Ann Fennelly **micro-memoirs**

Beth Ann Fennelly **poems**

Beth Ann Fennelly **ted talk**

Beth Ann Fennelly **biography**

Beth Ann Fennelly **sister**

The first time I saw this last related search, I was shocked. Shocked, but not for long.

When I thought about it, searching for my sister made a lot of sense. After all, I'm also searching for my sister, though in a different way, of course. The reader, I assume, is searching for the manner of her death.

I haven't been consciously withholding this from the reader—I haven't been consciously withholding anything from anyone besides myself—but I see now that this narrative gap could frustrate. I've written so much about grieving my sister, but I haven't said what happened. What happened, it's safe to say, has not been made available to users. Thus, users have fled into the many-armed embrace of Google.

In high school, just so you know, I was accused of being a tease.

The lesson seemed to be that if you make someone desire something, you'd better be prepared to hand it over.

You'd think I'd have learned my lesson. You'd think I'd have learned my lesson, and written it down, so we could quit searching.

PAGEANT
Joshilyn Jackson

It's funny how when people talk about when they were kids and they can only go back so far. Anything that happens to a baby gets eat up by things that happen after. Except it seems like whatever happened can still bother you later, and you won't know what's making you so crazy because it's lost. Maybe those kinds of things are what made my sister Crissy get divorced and become a whore.

Now me, I remember back early, like when I was first moved into a grown-up bed and I hated it and wanted my bars back. I felt stretched out on a hill where wolves could see me. I had a pig book with a wolf in it. He wasn't a cartoon wolf with clothes on, he was real, and I'd think of him and go searching my body for scrapes so I could lick and lick them, hoping I could lick away the blood smell, so he couldn't find me.

The older I get, though, the more I've got little memory holes, little blank patches in my grown years. My childhood, I can smell it, but the rest? Feels like God took a shotgun and made all the baby time I was supposed to lose into shot, and then fired into my life.

I don't even remember last time I saw Crissy. I'd married Chuck and I was pregnant with our second when she got divorced. Daddy said she was dead to all of us, and told me she had moved to Babylon, by which he meant New Orleans.

I don't remember even if she said goodbye, but I remember being picked for Mary. I can't hardly remember what my face looks like these days, but I can see myself so clear, thirteen, wearing a long shiny green dress with laces tight up the front, standing with all the Teens for Jesus in the fellowship hall while Mr. Larry handed out the roles.

Emma Leroy was right in front. She'd made more toilet paper roses for the tops of the Thanksgiving poor baskets than anyone and now she was going to be Mary or know there was no justice, no decency, and no one was listening to God. She hung around outside services and said all these things really loud to her friend Katy Preston, who had such bad skin that she would never be picked.

Katy stood real near Emma, like Emma getting picked would be like Katy winning. I crouched low in back and wished I was her. In Teens for Jesus if you teased or were mean Mr. Larry made you go to the altar during the invitation and ask for prayers to cleanse your hatefulness, so it was like her skin made her invisible. I wanted to go over and pick at it for her. I was standing in the back tearing little bits of my fingers off and then sucking them till the blood stopped.

Mr. Larry did the boys first because the boys never cared, then everyone else, even the shepherds, before he said real fast, "That leaves Emma to be our Innkeeper's Wife, which is a speaking part and very important, and Franny for Mary." Then he practically fled.

Emma stood there for a really long time while everyone started milling and getting purses and clearing out. I thought she was maybe going to cry, but then she turned on me and I could see it was a terrible rage, and she said, "You—you don't even have tits yet. How could you nurse the baby Jesus with no tits? Baby Jesus will die, die, die and it will be your fault and the whole world will go to hell."

I wanted to tell her that we could trade, that I would rather be boiled than be Mary. A big spotlight shone on Mary when the choir sang "Silent Night" and everyone looked and looked.

Crissy, who had had a real baby by then so couldn't play the holy virgin ever again no matter how long and blonde and perfect her hair was, stepped forward and said, "You ought to be ashamed talking about Virgin Mary's bosoms, you trash."

On the rehearsal night, I was getting ready to walk to Bethlehem with Joseph when Crissy stopped me because she noticed my white slippers were all over blood. She made me take them off and saw I had peeled the calluses off my feet until the soles of them were striped and bleeding.

The choir was about to finish "Oh, Holy Night" and then Joseph and I had to start walking.

"Franny, what'd you do?" Crissy said.

My eyes rolled back in my head and I sunk down onto the floor and said, "I'm like The Little Mermaid and I walk on knives," and I was clutching the swaddled baby doll we used for Jesus so hard that if it had been a real baby I would have killed it.

The choir stopped, and I heard Mr. Larry calling for us, "Joseph and Mary! Joseph and Mary!"

The back of my throat felt slick and hot and sour. I saw Crissy firm her mouth up and she hollered back, "Mr. Larry, Franny's sick."

Joseph stopped gawking down and bounded away from me like a scared deer, and I heard Emma say, real loud, "If Franny throws up on the baby Jesus, we will all go right to hell, right to hell this minute."

Crissy hollered, "Shut up, Emma, you dumb cow! Franny, think about ice and glaciers and polar bears," and then she dropped down beside me.

I told her, "I'm like that man on the pallet by the healing waters and I can never get up till Jesus comes."

She said, "Franny, if you don't, you are going to miss Christmas, so no ham dinner and Daddy is going to give your present to little poor children—now get up and follow me and I will tell Mr. Larry you can never be Mary, ever."

She was laughing, a little, but I could see her eyes were serious. I did it. What she said. I got up and followed her, and I never did have to be Mary.

When I close my eyes, I can see that day so perfect. But maybe not, because it's like I'm watching me like I was a movie, from the outside, not from inside my own eyes. And anyway, I never owned a long green shiny dress that laced up tight. I think the prize girls on *The Price Is Right* wore that today. They always have that on in the rec room here. I watch it, but I ask that one nice girl with the braids to wheel me around backward if they are showing games with cards or dice.

No, I never had a shiny, tight dress like that, and if I had, I wouldn't have wore it. Maybe none of it happened the way I see it in my head at all. But I think it did, and here's what's true: If Crissy came to me right now and said, "Follow me, just follow me," I'd get up even if my feet were bleeding, even if I left red tracks that any wolf could follow. I'd stand up beside my sister, and I'd go.

MIMI, 1968
Suzanne Kingsbury

Paulie married Mimi at four in the afternoon under the trellis in his mama's yard. When the breeze blew, you could smell the honeysuckle and the priest sweating camphor and wine. Behind them lay the graveyard and all those silent stones.

I was best man. Mimi never took her eyes from Paulie the whole time. She wore a dress the color of buttermilk and flowers in her hair and talked so soft, we had to lean in to hear. The priest held her hand so long, finally Paulie had to take it back.

His mama had hung paper lanterns in the trees, and a pinata where the tire swing used to be. There were punch glasses filled with gin and a cake said, *Congratulations, we'll miss you!* His mother sat on the porch swing and cried. In a black-and-white photograph by the cut-up sandwiches, his father wore all those Korean medals across his chest.

After midnight, Paulie brought out hashish, and it was like flying, everything lit up. Teeth, t-shirts and socks shone and floated by. I went past the treeline, where Paulie and I used to play army and lay on my back. The stars looked like a million little eyes that didn't care if we lived or died. I knew Paulie'd see the same where he went in Nam.

When I woke, my neck had a tie rod in it and my foot was asleep. I hobbled on. The pinata had been broken and the porch door was open to the den. I should've gone inside. But I went around front, and I saw them standing in the lake, her legs around Paulie's waist. I could hear the sound of their breathing, carried across the lake, so still it was a mirror, and all the stars had fallen in.

I'd spent my tarring money that spring on a '65 Plymouth Sport Fury two-door hardtop, put a blower between the manifold and the carburetors and let her run. And now I rolled it outta there. Going around the lake, I got up around eighty. When I hit corners, I'd brake, almost tail-spinning on every one. I drove around again and again, thinking of her at the carnival last June, how he lifted her up on the carousel to watch her ride. We sat on the mayor's stone wall the next day in the hot smell of tar, watching his kid push a mower around the yard and eating peanut-butter and jelly sandwiches Paulie's mother packed.

"I'm gonna marry her," Paulie said. "Low number or not. I got this feeling I'll make it out."

"You got jelly on your mouth," I told him.

I'd sidekicked Paulie long enough to know, he'd come back all right. He'd been winning all his life. Prom king, captain of everything, teachers' favorite and number one, always, with the girls. Blond shock of hair, muscles that defined a shirt and skin that browned as soon as the summer came. Paulie'd never hurt for love.

The ride around the lake was just under five miles and took seven minutes. Try as I might, I couldn't go any faster. The houses started to blur. The pass kept coming up sooner than I expected, but seven minutes was all I got. I saw her in her white bathing suit last Fourth of July, her hair slick down the back. I'd been holding Nellie's hand. When I dropped it, Nellie said, "What?" But she knew. You couldn't not know, when Mimi climbed that ladder to the dock, putting her arms up to Paulie, who looked stronger when he held her.

Around Butch's store, the sheriff lights went on, and I braked, sat there waiting, my window down.

Shepell opened my door. "Just from your breath, I could give you a 502." His uniform was so well ironed, it could've moved without him. "Let me drive you home."

"Fuck you will."

"How'd Paulie's wedding go?"

"Remember when you were a panty-waist kissee?" I asked him. "How the hell is it you give me orders now and carry a gun?" I got out. But I couldn't quite stand and had to hold the door.

"Paulie leaves today?" he asked it so quiet, it almost wasn't said.

In the back of his car, I realized I was shoeless.

Shep glanced in the rearview. "What's the matter with you? Out here alone, you didn't even have your radio on."

I watched the houses go by and didn't answer.

The day the draft got called, Paulie'd come over. His number was 45. Mine was five. He said, "Twitchin' out's a good thing today," talking of my epilepsy, which felt like a cliche. "Let's celebrate."

We went to Butch's store and bought a bottle of Ballantine.

Sometime around noon, we'd fired up our old go-carts and raced them around the overgrown track we'd built back when there were no girls or wars. He'd been winning, until I rode up beside him on the crabgrass rise, where the track goes skinny. He almost flipped, but the engine crapped out when the cart grounded on a mound. After the dust settled, I saw him squinting at me like he'd just seen me for the first time.

When I got out of Shepell's car, I sat on my porch steps. I didn't think they were in the lake anymore, but I was clear across the opposite side and truth be told, I couldn't really see, though I strained my eyes. I thought maybe Paulie'd come by. I thought about my physical and how I'd told them what I had, the word foreign compared to the stick in my teeth and Paulie over me when I had a fit, his eyes wide and his lip sweaty, shaking me, saying, "You didn't eat your tongue at least. I heard that happens. How's your head?" Clouds passed. Paulie asked, "You want me to tell you what you did?" But I hadn't wanted to hear how my eyes rolled and my limbs went on with a mind of their own, like guys shot in movies.

I had a cigarette in my pocket someone gave me at Paulie's, and a pack of matches from the hash, so I smoked. It made me feel a little sick. Across the lake, the sun rose red, not the sun itself but its mention. I knew I wouldn't make it to Paulie's bus.

I started going there as soon as he left.

At first I just stood on the walk and she half-sat on the railing. "I just come by to see how's it going," I said.

"I'm all right," she said. "He hasn't written yet."

"He will. You call me if you want to."

She nodded. I knew she'd cry when I left. In July she started making those mojitos. She said she found the recipe in a summer magazine. They had real mint floating in them. Her mama worked the town hall and her daddy was manager at the mill, so no one was home while we got slowly sloshed, a color like magenta sinkers high on her cheeks.

"I guess before me, Paulie never really thought he'd settle

down," she said. "You were the one supposed to marry first." She brought out the annual. We looked at Paulie's picture. *Most Likely to Break Hearts.* He looked tall. I was smaller than him by half-a-foot. I lay on her porch floor, the summer so hot it made liquid of your limbs, and she said, "We'll name her Angie if she's a girl." Her hair, tied in a yellow scarf, ran like a blonde fountain between her pregnant breasts

"And if she's a boy?"

She laughed, swinging, her dress lifting to her thighs. "Paulie," she said.

When she cried, she never made a sound, just wiped her tears. Then she'd go inside, the screen door slamming, and blow her nose.

Early August, we watched them harvest the corn behind her house. By and by the stalks would break like skinny legs. I knew the day I asked her why she cried was the last one we'd spend outside.

Her eyes were the color of the sky at high noon, pale blue. She said how the baby scared her, the war. She wished she'd graduated high school. She didn't know Paulie in those letters he wrote, even if he came back, it'd be another boy she'd have to learn to love. She couldn't climb back in time and be sixteen again.

I didn't mean to pick her up like a bride and bring her into the house, lay her on her bed with Paulie's picture on the dresser to our right. I didn't mean her to touch me with that tiny diamond on her finger. I didn't even know I knew how to do it: kiss smooth the taught skin holding the baby in.

After the first time, I understood it wasn't her I was after. It was Paulie I wanted to be. When I kissed her, placed my hand between her legs, I was Paulie, and she was looking at me that day beneath the trellis, the drunk priest between us, and all those silent stones, spread out behind our backs.

DANCE TO THE MUSIC
from *BACK HOME: A VIETNAM VETERAN'S WIFE'S SHORT MEMOIR ABOUT A LONG WAR*
Bev Marshall

I was not Kelly's friend. I was Dave's. Like most of the wives in class 68A in pilot school in Laredo, Texas, I didn't like her very much. Maybe we wives were a little bit jealous of Kelly who as a single girl danced with all the young pilots at the Officers Club. We married wives were protective of the single men, distrustful of the local girls who flooded into the O'Club looking for free drinks hoping to land a pilot with a guaranteed government paycheck. Kelly was one of them. She wasn't a ballerina or a tap dancer or a high-kicker like the Rockettes. She was a Watusi dancer, a lithe and limber sexy girl who could twist and shout and knock herself out on the dance floor. Many weekends I watched Kelly and her various partners dance to the beat of The Animals, Credence Clearwater, The Righteous Brothers. One of her partners was Dave. He was one of the few pilots who could shake and slide with Kelly on the polished hardwood floors beside the bar.

Before pilot school ended, Dave confided to us that he was in love. Kelly was, he said, the most perfect woman he'd ever met. "She's smart about jets. She understands about pulling G's, knows what a fuselage is," he said. I knew those things too. So what? I wanted to say. And I was a good dancer too . . . but maybe not as good as Kelly.

They were married in the base chapel. There was no time for a honeymoon. Dave had orders to begin training the following week in the F-4 that he would fly over Vietnam.

Kelly didn't accompany Dave to George Air Base in California. She told me that he would need to concentrate on learning to fly his plane. She'd be a distraction and she wanted him to be an expert stick. His skills could mean the difference between life and death in a war. All true but I couldn't imagine giving up those precious weeks with Butch. Maybe she was being a stronger military wife. Not one of us whiny wives dependent on our husbands for happiness.

Kelly moved to Dallas. She'd been there for less than a month when she called me. "Hey Bev I was just wondering how you're liking living with your parents."

Was she kidding? Who wanted parental supervision as an adult? "It's okay I guess," I said.

"Well, I've got a proposition for you. Come to Dallas and we can share this great apartment. We'll be roommates . . . like you had in college."

She went on detailing the glories of Dallas at some length. The mix of tall buildings and peaceful parks, it was pristine and sure did appeal to her having lived in Laredo where brown dust covered her car and most buildings were no more than three stories tall.

"Sounds nice," I said, "but I'm trying to get a teaching job here in Gulfport."

"That's the other great thing. Jobs are easy to find here in a big city. I've already got a job in a big insurance company. I handle the paperwork for claims for all kinds of things. Auto accidents, house fires, burglaries, you wouldn't believe how much money people get for just losing a ring they insured."

I told Kelly it all sounded exciting but I'd have to pass. Butch wanted me to be near the families. "They help me out a lot," I said.

I asked her about Dave. She told me he was based in Udon in Thailand and he wrote to her nearly every day. "He signs his letters 'Your Dance Partner for Life'," she said with a giggle. She and Dave, like Butch and I, dreamed about R & R in Hawaii and she was working on a tan. She wanted to look fabulous in a bikini on Waikiki Beach.

Kelly called me once more before she disappeared. She thought maybe I'd reconsider and come to Dallas. "There's this great club just a few blocks from where I live. Name bands and plenty of guys to dance with. We could show them all a thing or two on the dance floor," she said. "Everyone is really friendly. You'd have so much fun."

I hadn't danced since Butch left and I admit having fun with people who weren't my relatives appealed to me, but I was a married woman. And so is she I thought.

"It's tempting, Kelly," I said, "but I'll have to pass again."

I asked about Dave and she said he was flying long missions.

"Really his letters are getting kind of boring. Same thing. Working a lot. Tired. Nothing too exciting to share."

"Well, that's good, isn't it? That means he's okay. Safe."

"Oh yes, of course. I just meant I'm tired of letters. I'm wanting him to come home so we can have fun together again. Nobody at the club can dance like him."

We didn't have much else to say and our call ended soon. As I hung up, I wondered why Kelly had chosen me instead of some other wife she'd met in Laredo. What impression had I given her that would make her think I'd want to live with her, dance with other men? All of us wives were lonely certainly. We all missed making love, having our men in our lives. Hell I missed Butch's filthy socks and I wouldn't complain if I had to sew on 100 flight suit patches if I could have him back home.

I never heard from Kelly again but a year and a half later Butch ran into Dave in Thailand. Dave had a story to tell. It began with him strapping in the F-4 behind the pilot in the front seat, Fitch. Dave said he saw the terrain below him, knew they were just north of the DMZ, 400 knots, 500, descending to 1,000 feet. Then the sound, the jolt, and before he had understood they were hit, Fitch in the front seat initiated the ejection sequence. "I wasn't ready," Dave said. "No! Wait!" But he was already out, his leg, his arm. Pain. He knew his body had hit the plane as if he were the firepower. Chute is open. Okay, but he can't see and then the trees. More pain. And the chute is caught. It's got the signal he knows, but he's hanging and his arm can't reach the release. "And there were ants," he said. Ants crawling, crawling inside his suit, across his face, hundreds of them. He has to find the release, but it's dark, so dark. He hears them, the chatter of their foreign tongues. They've seen the chute floating. Oh god, will they see it floating above them, can they see through the foliage? Don't look up, don't, don't, don't. Quiet, don't breathe. Don't move. Their voices fade and he's got the release, but it's too far to the ground. Falling through the branches and there's nothing. The world gone black.

Rescue came, but Dave now had a stiff leg, a cane. He told Butch about his injuries. Broken arms, ribs, the femur in his left leg. Several surgeries. "But I was lucky," he said. "Not an amputee and now disability and I'm catching hops all over the globe. His buddy Fitch didn't make it out. His body, or what was left of it, was recovered.

Dave had another story. Kelly was in Dallas when she got the news about Dave's crash, but she wasn't told the extent of his injuries, only that they were serious. "Before she came to the hospital, she called me, said she was nervous, had been to a hospital only once when her little brother fell out of a tree and had a mild concussion. We laughed that both of her patients had a problem with trees."

Dave's doctor, Colonel Richardson, met Kelly in the waiting room and later told Dave he'd explained the extent of his injuries in detail so that Kelly would understand that her husband would require extensive care, rehabilitation. "The Doc stopped by, looked around the room and said, 'Where's your wife'?" I told him she hadn't come in. Told him how happy I was she would arrive soon. 'I can hardly stand the wait,' I said. Doc didn't tell me he'd seen her already."

Where had Kelly gone? Dave still doesn't know, but an hour passed before she opened the door to Dave's shared room. "She looked like a movie star. Blonde hair grown out long and she always had those big tits. Man, I wanted to eat her up. But she just stood there at the door. I knew I looked like Frankenstein, all bandages and tubes. When she didn't come closer, I said, 'Helluva sight, aren't I'?"

Kelly had nodded, taken steps toward him as he pushed back the sheet across his body.

Dave said, "I tried to joke, said, 'Come see what's left of me. Come kiss me. Come come come.' She didn't smile. She just stared at me and then I saw the fear, maybe revulsion. I dunno. Something. And she backed up, backed up. All she said was, 'I can't do this.' That was it. Can't do it and she was out the door."

Dave got the divorce papers before he finished rehab.

REHAB
Janet Nodar

We damaged people sit in our circle of orange plastic chairs
and imitate Heather. We make little movements with our legs and arms.
Those of us who are strong enough stretch long rubber bands or move
weighted poles up and down. Sweet Heather never ceases to smile. Her
shiny brown ponytail bobs whcn shc moves her head. She's cheerful in
the therapy rooms, too, tender with the uncertain, even though we can
take seconds to lift a hand to a pulley, a foot to a treadmill. A sudden
disruption in the brain and we woke to being aged infants, unstable and
tremulous.

Heather understands this, even if only in theory. She is young
and strong and can look at an arm or leg or hand and list the muscles
and nerves encased within. I saw her eyes very clearly once (as clearly
as if we were lovers). We were in line at the water fountain, I itching in
my wheelchair, and she tilted toward me and asked me if I was having
a nice day. I said yes. I'm not out to cause trouble. Her eyes are bright
brown, penny-colored. Shards of green radiate out from the pupils.
The green is not evenly distributed; there is more in the right eye than
the left. It means nothing, of course. A detail. A trick of genetics. The
sort of thing you know about people you love. Our eyes met, but I
didn't feel that I was seeing into Heather's soul.

It's a myth that you can see into a woman's heart by looking
into her eyes. You can never see into another person's heart. You see
only the reflection of your own. This seems like something to regret,
but I'm not convinced. Maybe it should be enough just to see her. To
say: here is a woman. Her eyes are beautiful.

Anyway, on that day Heather was kind enough to hand me
a paper cup. We are hygienic here at rehab. The staff is constantly
vacuuming, organizing the magazines, wiping down the treadmills with
Formula 409. We don't drink straight out of the water fountain, but
wait in line and fill our paper cups, a step that intervenes between thirst
and water, that makes our lives more orderly. At the end of the day

76

there will be a row of plastic bags filled with our buoyant trash.

Heather wears a cheap engagement ring. Her boyfriend comes in late sometimes and lifts weights, waiting for her to get off work. They're in love. This in itself is not interesting, I know. Love is not rare and precious. It's thick on the ground, and there's nothing more tiresome than the newly dazzled, locked in each other's high-beams. I remember. The simplest conversation hums with covert meaning. You feel the current coursing. You think that if you can just say, just do, the one true thing, she won't turn away from you. For years, well after I knew that even the right woman would not complete me, hope could still act on me like a poison.

Don't think I'm a cynic. I'm not ungrateful. Fortune still smiles on me. For example, I have Doris, my attendant, who drives me to my sessions at rehab. We're not friends, but we get along. She takes me to see my doctors too, and to the stores, the library. My taste disappoints her. She frowns and shakes her head at my thrillers and westerns. Doris could exercise while the therapists attend to me, but she won't. The suggestion makes her laugh. It makes me laugh too, really. I know what she thinks when she looks at me. What's the point of all this busywork? I'm made of meat and blood, like everyone else, but my time is running out. I need a taxidermist, not a doctor.

My daughter Cheryl hired Doris. My Cheryl remains blond, just another example of her diligence. She's the most fretful of my children. Her laughter never carries conviction. Her worries are like ants. They gorge on any small crumb, and somehow free her from seeing the corpse lying across the path. All of my children work to hide their dismay at what is left of their father. They don't want to hurt me. They want to be good. That's the legacy of their mother, who also wanted to be good. Her sustaining belief: sooner or later, I'd get what I deserved. And now she isn't here to see me trembling. I fought her so ferociously for my little wants. What do I want now? A dish of ice cream. A handful of Seconal. An orgasm. An orgasm? Oh, yes: I remember. The honeyed trance; the idiot thrust; the woman breathing my name.

To be honest, I was not prepared for adulthood. The complacent town where I grew up, the closed circuit of my father's house, my little rebellions, sufficient to shatter my mother's assumptions: these things misled me. I expected something more significant. I expected to matter more. Eventually, though, I saw that none of us were prepared. How can you get ready? I remember rising above a green jungle in a helicopter, my shattered leg wrapped in a bloody blanket (this was the first time I met with mortality), floating in a sea of noise and heat and pain so intense it emptied me out, a poured cup. The sun was in the sky. It lit us, and the trees below us, and I was nothing, a pulse and a set of eyes, and yet my heart lifted, suddenly joyous. I did not question. I just thought, I'm here. I am still here.

Now, once again, I'm forced to meditate. I'm no longer a man of action. I look around me: these people don't know what fuels them. The skin tells lies. The woman touching my arm, my leg—she doesn't love me. She's only a therapist. This is her vocation, her selected chore. If she loves me it is only in the abstract, as one admires an idea, a principle. Yet my body records her touch. I don't suspect her of affection, but I know she's alive, I know her heart beats, and she knows the same of me.

Years ago, when my children were small, the requirements of my job temporarily took me away from home. It seemed foolish, even selfish, to uproot the family from our leafy suburb, the familiar schools, the malls—and so I went alone. I lived in a new city, in a furnished apartment. It came with spoons, with cups and books, with a clock and a white bed. A few towels; that was all I added. I was exhilarated. A new life, without losing the old, without the weight of permanence. It was a gift. I was of course thinking of sex. Not love. Well, perhaps love. And certainly sex, the marrow of love.

The girl I met, the real girl, her eyes were brown also, but darker than our Heather's, so dark as to be almost black, pupil and iris merged. She was a clerk. She answered phones and filed papers. She had nothing, except youth and beauty. The very walls melted when I saw her. Naturally, I—older, moneyed, married—had the upper hand. Yet I seemed to need her, and she could not help responding to me, even though she was a clever girl. So we were together in the white bed. The skin lies, yes, but she breathed my name from her heart; that, I believe.

I had not imagined that I could be tempted, that love could

suddenly seem a living thing. I hadn't imagined regret. I hadn't imagined her crying. Soon the bed, our oasis, wasn't sufficient. Why did she want so much more than I had to give? Really, she was foolish. She was too young for compromise. I had encouraged her to dream—really, that was the extent of my crime. She denied me the expiation of kindness. That was her cruelty. Eventually she went off to be happy with someone else, and I admit it was a relief to me.

It grieves me, here at the slack end of my life, that I cannot remember her face more specifically. There was a woman; her eyes were beautiful—but the years have corroded me. I wish I'd never wanted anything from her. I wish generosity had come more easily to both of us. I remember the beat of the rotor blades, and the sun in the trees. I remember my father's house and hear my daughter's uncertain laugh. I wish I'd been kinder to my wife. Her little wants; they were not less important than my own.

WHAT WAR WILL DO, 1968
Suzanne Kingsbury

I go to the Depot Saturday nights, takes the ouch out. No girl wants a guy with a bum leg, you got to buy your comfort. Ma says legs got nothing to do with it. She's the tailor and got so much work, one, two o'clock in the morning that machine's going. An old beat up thing the color of a swimming pool, keeps us flush. I don't got my own money coming, on account of dishonorable discharge.

Margit opens the door and looks me and the crutches over with those nail gray eyes. "You think you can behave yourself?"

I spit in the dirt and tell her I think so.

"You can't have her," she says, meaning Lynne. "You'll have another one."

"I'll pay double for her." I try to look sheepish, good.

She surveys me with her gray square eyes. I armpit the crutches and dig inside my denims to show her the money.

"You touch her untoward and I'll shoot you with my 12 gauge and bury you under the depot like a dog." When I hand over the money, she turns and leaves the door open, so I can come inside.

Tommy Orton's here, with some who didn't go to Nam or came back whole. I look at the threadbare carpet. They say, "That fat redhead with the big tits working tonight?" "You got that one with the tattoo on her butt of a gun?" "You got that black chick from Buffalo?"

Margit says, "Keep it in your pants, sweetheart, she's coming fast as she can." Then the cargo train hits and everything the whores own rattles like a set of teeth. When I look up, Lynne's at the top of the stairs, wearing the dress with the fringe, her black hair's cut like a French girl and that lazy eye looks whitish blue like the leg the first days I took the bandage off. She touches her neck when she sees me, quick, and blinks.

She writes her name on the chart, and I follow her upstairs, hoisting myself up. The bum leg sounds like a bullet on the wood. The dress is gingham, she's told me four hundred times. She bought it in the city, it's handmade. Lynne's a blue streak talker, it's how she got in trouble last time, but usually that voice keeps me occupied. I glance at that dime-sized neck scar. Her slipper heels drag, they sound like rain on a pane of glass.

Her room is in the rafters. You can see the blind guy playing his organ from there. She's got an iron headboard with cheese cloth over it, Lynne says is her canopy, she always wanted one as a little girl.

Her eyes follow me when she lies on the bed, like she's watching a snake, to see will it strike. I tell her to get under the covers, take off all her clothes and close her eyes. I lean my crutches against the wall, sit on the bed and take off my clothes, too.

In the dark I look down at it, shriveled like the leg of a turkey you kill at Christmas. I tell her keep your eyes closed, then pull up the covers and don't think about how many men been where I'm about to go.

She smells like oranges and she says "oh" when you take off her panties, like it's a big surprise, like she wasn't just with the judge and his brother, his brother's cousin and his friend. Like she didn't lie there, soft, for the whole town. She moves awkward, when you put your hand over her mouth, the other one over her eyes. She don't got a confident tongue, she's like the twelve-year old cousin in the backyard you have to teach how to do it right and watch out for the teeth. But Lynne's got a softness to her you might die in. You want to nail it down, make it cry. I close my eyes and truth is, I fly. Even through the pain.

Downstairs the organ plays and you slump over like a god-damn rattler who just ate.

Lynne don't hurry me out. That's what makes you think you might be more than just money for her morning milk, even though your second hour is twice as much as the first. I wait. Maybe on account of last time, she's got a new stiffness, like a chord somewhere been pulled too tight. I take out a Lucky Strike and reach for the lighter off an old apple crate. We lay quiet while the blind guy plays something crazy beautiful on the organ. Usually she can't help but talk, she's got a mouth like a radio, won't stop. A voice on stilts, hurried but unsure, stops and starts all over the place.

Downstairs, the door bells sound. Margit says, "Just a minute hon." I think of my mother at that machine, the maddening sound when I'm trying to sleep. Lynne lays there, staring at the ceiling. The smoke rises to a bird's nest. It's weird, a bird's nest in a whore's house, it wasn't there before.

Lynne don't study me like she did last time, when she dragged her fingers down my arm, I almost felt like I'd cry, how nice it felt. She'd asked what it felt like, going berserk, nutso, willy wonka like they said. What was it like to do that to my leg? It'd come to me hard, that acute, sharp pain, how out of your skin you went when the aura came, everything broken up like a kaleidoscope, nothing fit together right. She told me she'd heard I'd been put in a jacket and tied to a table.

They all knew I'd done the leg bad in base camp, never made it over there. The idea came early on, like weather, I couldn't stop it. And the M16 sitting in my hand, they'd issued it. Course someone's gonna be nuts if they shoot their leg off, you either die of pain or go insane. "You could've lived had you gone," Lynne had said, her hands like feathers against my throat, "maybe nothing woulda happened to you. Nothing happened to Tommy Orton."

The feeling to do it had started in my groin, all the blood settled there and rose. Lynne had been saying how her old man lost his marbles, too. She'd seen him in the city with twigs in his beard, wearing lady's slippers, but he hadn't done it on account of war, and that's when I burned her. Put the Lucky Strike below her ear, which God help me is softer than every other part of her.

She tried to scramble, but I put my bum leg over her and pressed hard. She started screaming like a child and Margit came running with a team of whores, "you fucking goon, you shithouse crazy no good pussy-loving son-of-a-bitch quit the fucking army and all those kids are dying brave."

I can feel Lynne breathing next to me now, the softness comes off her like the citrus smell, I stayed away as long as I could before that softness come hunting me up again. "You smoke that any lower you're gonna be sucking your hand," she finally says and takes it from me. I can see the scar when she turns to stub out the smoke and feel all the sudden I might throw up. I tell her to close her eyes and I get dressed. "Don't open 'em." I keep my eyes on her when I back out.

I can smell spring on the lake outside, that cracked ice and liquid mud. Last time, after I'd burned her and they kicked me out, it'd started snowing. I'd slipped and fallen on the road. My jacket was back in the whore house. I thought maybe I'd freeze out there. It was after midnight. There'd been a moon out. My mother doesn't sleep well in a waxing moon. I pictured her sewing the whole town's clothes and eventually found my way up on the crutches.

Now the smell of spring makes me start running, dragging the bum leg behind me, the crutches planting themselves as fast as I can make them. I remember one time we were kids and played kickball at Elem schoolyard, I kicked it so hard, they had to go over the fence to get it. Tommy Orton made a rule at the beginning of the summer, you could get as many home runs as you wanted from one kick. I made twelve that day. They carried me home on their shoulders. I could hear my name in my ears.

I can't run for long on account of the ache. The lake looks like them craters you see in movies where the earth blows up, or a meteor burns a hole so big you fall in and land in China. I might kill Lynne someday, kill the softness right out of her. Her mouth will go off like a radio, and I won't be able to help it.

My mom's inside, bent over the machine. "You'll never make it out of there," she told me like a broken record player before I left, "those boys are getting paralyzed from their eyebrows to their toes, na-palmed, brain dead, burned alive." She drilled it into me like a pound-ing needle in the head.

She drove seventeen hours to get me at the base camp hospital. "All it took was one leg." She told me. "You got another."

I turn the knob and step in. "Ma," I say. "I'm home."

SEVEN DAYS
from *BACK HOME: A VIETNAM VETERAN'S WIFE'S
SHORT MEMOIR ABOUT A LONG WAR*
Bev Marshall

"Being with you and not being with you is the only way I have to measure time."
—Jorge Luis Borges

DAY TWO

Kauai is all I'd dreamed it would be after I read in the brochure that the musical, *South Pacific*, was filmed here at Hanalei Plantation. I've seen the movie twice and know all the songs by heart. In fact, I feel like a movie star myself in this beautiful room. The glass wall looks down onto a private cove. White sheers hang from bamboo rods around the bed, and the bathroom vanity is red-veined marble. On the round table overlooking the cove sits a "Welcome" basket of fruit: oranges, pineapple, mangoes, and bananas.

He jumps on the bed and pats the space beside him. "Come here," he says. "What a view!"

I lie beside him, suddenly shy. It's been such a long time since I've been with a man. When he'd made love to me last night, I'd been someone else. Some fictional woman who knew how to welcome her man home properly. Now I'm stuck with who I am and he isn't the familiar man I married three years ago. He's a warrior now.

I squeeze my eyes shut as he slides his briefs down his golden-haired legs. When he blows on my stomach, my eyes fly open and I laugh as I wiggle down. I sigh when he kisses me quiet.

DAY FOUR

We walk along the rocky shoreline. He talks about things he

84

hasn't written about in his letters. As he tells me about landing on makeshift strips of land carved out of the jungle, of mortar fire that hits the underbelly of the Caribou he's piloting, of the Vietnamese he's relocated out of harm's way, I understand that he has fallen in love with the military. I can't comprehend these tales of short field landings and flaps and ailerons, and evasive maneuvers in the sky. When I talk about the Charles Dickens projects my students have accomplished, his gaze drifts out toward China. I fall silent and walk ahead. From behind his arms reach out to encircle me. He pulls me close. "Let's go back to the room," he says.

I dress for dinner. I wiggle my breasts into the padded push up bra. The pale pink sundress shimmies down over my body. I pirouette; the full skirt billows around me in soft waves. He catches me mid-turn. He whispers, "You're beautiful and sexy." I smile. He's such a good liar.

I eat the prawns the dignified waiter has set down with a flourish on the patio table. Unused to dining in fancy restaurants, I don't know how to respond to his obsequious manner. He doesn't notice the waiter. He's talking with his hands now, flying his palms over his empty plate. He smokes a cigar and the blue smoke drifts into my hair and I think that he seems far older than I. He's only twenty-four but he has the eyes of a battle-tested soldier. In three days he'll be a soldier again and I'll be boarding a plane back to Mississippi. I duck my head, take a breath, and then lift my eyes to his.

"I know," he says.

DAY SEVEN

I open my eyes and close them shut. I don't want this day to begin. I don't want to pack my clothes into my new luggage. I don't want to go to the airport in Honolulu. I don't want him to go back to Saigon. He shakes me. "Time to get going," he says. His eyes are red, puffy. He hasn't slept either. We don't talk as I fold my shorts and tops, as he stuffs his swimsuit into the green duffel bag. We check the drawers, the bathroom shelf, beneath the bed. There is nothing left to pack. It's time to call the cab.

The Pan American gate agent tells us where to go to board the plane that will carry all the men on R&R back to their bases and posts. There will be a short delay. We see the big white and blue plane on the tarmac. I don't know how many passengers it will hold, but I think maybe two hundred. I turn and see that the waiting room is crowded now.

There are three hundred or more people, men, women, a few children, and a couple of babies in this glass-walled room. The men are dressed in uniforms of every branch of the service, a collage of Army green, brown khaki, Air Force blue, Navy white and black. Some of the soldiers can't be more than eighteen, some of the wives even younger. There are no old people in the room. At least one hundred people are already crying, some silently, others moaning with their wails. Everyone is kissing, hugging, clinging to someone. An announcement blares out, "Time to board, men. Let's go."

Everyone falls silent. I cling to him for this last kiss, and I know that many of these women are kissing their husbands for the last time ever. I know I could be one of them. A young boy drops to a chair and sobs. I hear his wife say, "Don't go. Stay." A soldier pats the young girl's shoulder as he walks by.

I stand watching Butch's back until he disappears. When the door to the jet way closes, the silence in the room is unbearable. I hear my breath, the inhalation of the girl standing next to me. I move away almost tiptoeing to the window. I see the plane sitting on the runway now like a giant bomb that will blow up the lives of the families in this room. I see the frightened drawn faces at the window. As the women and children watch the plane slowly begin to taxi away, the sound of their breaths can't be heard anymore. They're all holding them in. I watch the plane until it turns on the taxiway, and I lean my forehead against the glass. It is cool on my sunburn, and I feel water running down my legs from the blisters breaking behind my knees. No one leaves the room. Everyone knows that some of us will be widows within months or even weeks. Some of the children in this room won't have a father to toss them a ball, to tuck them into bed, to teach them to drive or swim or fish or share any of life's lessons. I drop down onto the plastic chairs; some of the women continue standing at the window as if expecting the plane to reappear. Finally, a baby cries from across the room, and then a torrent of sobs erupts. I see several girls sink to the floor, two of them are pregnant, and I think maybe I could be one of them now. Maybe I'm carrying an egg inside my womb at this moment and a baby of our own will be the gift of this trip. But somehow I know that my womb is as barren as my heart, and I pick up my carry-on and walk away from the carnage, the obscenity of war.

NEARING MARS
Doug Kelley

> I went to the woods because I wished to live
> deliberately, to front only the essential facts of life, and
> see if I could not learn what it had to teach, and not,
> when I came to die, discover that I had not lived.
>
> —Henry Thoreau

The night takeoff from Runway 8 in Albuquerque was smooth—the thunderstorm that slipped down from the Sandia Mountains and invaded the airport had moved away and dissipated. Other storms, small in size but magnificent in electrical display, had lingered over the mountains for most of the evening, but now they, too, were little more than ghostly wisps of their former selves.

Save for one lone remnant of storm, its cloud tops diffusing in the moonlight like Einstein's hair, the path to the east, back to Arkansas and hearth and home, was clear.

In a matter of minutes, we rose above the peaks and banked around the dying storm top, climbing away to the east. Steve and I settled into our cockpit seats, surrounded by the cocoon of switches, gauges, and glowing panel lights. Looking back into the cabin of the Dassault Falcon business jet, I saw the passengers, engaged in their small talk. One or two were reading. Briefcases were left closed, the work inside staying where it belonged. Some had drinks, but most just leaned back against the headrests, eyes closed.

It had been a long day.

Albuquerque fell behind, and the sparse landscape of New Mexico dropped away below the airplane. In the distance, the lights of Tucumcari came into view. Soon they would pass below, along with all the other lights of civilization.

Taking their place were lights from above. A nearly full moon lighted the world, washing out many of the stars. Still, I leaned forward, my face near the glare shield, watching the night sky. I recognized the constellation of Cassiopeia and thought of the John Masefield quote, "All I ask is a tall ship and a star to steer her by."

The bright moon also dimmed the chances of seeing any meteors, those streaks of star dust burning up in the atmosphere. It was August, and the Perseid shower was due.

Looking out the windshield on his side of the cockpit, Steve said, "Where are they?"

"It's early. The best time is the hours before dawn. Three or four in the morning."

"I'm not staying up that long."

"It's only a few more hours."

"I'm still not staying up."

I smiled. "We do have Mars, though," I said, nodding toward a bright object not far from the moon.

"That's Mars?"

"Yeah."

"Closest it's ever been, they say."

"Well," I said, "closest in a while, at least."

"Hasn't been this close for sixty thousand years."

"That's a while."

I thought of the astronomers, perched on their stools, peering through their telescopes, figuring out things like that.

We flew on, crossing into Texas.

"Doesn't look all that close to me," Steve said.

"It's still thirty-five million miles away," I said.

I glanced down, back inside the cockpit, looking over the instruments. Everything was as it should be. The autopilot was doing its job. I considered the altimeter. Flight Level 410. About forty-one thousand feet.

I looked over at Steve. "You know what, though? Right now we are about seven miles closer than most people."

Steve looked back at me, absorbing what I was saying. Then he laughed out loud.

Traveling a mile every eight seconds, we sped eastward, feeling privileged.

AN EXPLOSION WHEN YOU SEE ONE
Jason Headley

"You shouldn't be smoking."

"What are you, my doctor?"

"No, I mean the explosives. You shouldn't be smoking around the explosives."

Birddog had a knack for that. Running his mouth about things he barely understood. Kurt didn't understand much either, but at least he had the good sense to keep quiet about it. They'd been friends for so long, Kurt wasn't sure he had a say in the matter anymore. Not like with Katy. They got married, it was a disaster, they got divorced. Easy. With Birddog, there was no "for better or worse." "They're just fireworks, Birddog."

"So?"

"So they aren't explosives."

"Like hell. One of them Roman candles would knock your eye clean out of its socket."

"Just blow 'em up!" someone shouted from the bottom of the hill.

Kurt sighed and pressed his cigarette to the fuse of a bottle rocket he'd planted in the damp soil. The string hissed to life then launched into the blackness on a red rail. A snap of re-elicited cheers from the drunks in the valley below. Bits of grey paper lilted down onto Kurt and Birddog, sticking to their skin in the July swelter. Kurt pointed at the sky. "You call that an explosion?"

"Hold it in your hand then. Blow your damn finger off."

Kurt studied the pile of fireworks in the wheelbarrow. Bottle rockets, Roman candles, firecrackers, cone fountains, and something called the Apache Firedance. Birddog had pooled everyone's money before he left for Myrtle Beach two weeks ago with Katy. "Explosions all night!" That's what he'd promised. So everyone pitched in—three bucks here, five there—authorizing Birddog to fill his car with Chinese ingenuity and fill their patriot skies with fire. Kurt looked at Birddog sitting on a stump, nursing a sweaty can of beer. "I thought you wanted me to help you do this."

"I did."

"I'm not helping. I'm doing it all myself."

"What do you want me to do?"

"Whatever you'd do if I wasn't here."

Birddog walked to the wheelbarrow and sifted fireworks with his hand. "I just thought we could talk up here."

Kurt looked away and set off the Roman candles he'd fixed in a row. They whistled a rainbow blaze, drawing another slurry of joy from the crowd. The smoke drifted back and softly broke around Kurt, then Birddog. That was the order with them. Always. Birddog had been three months behind Kurt in getting married. Then three months behind him in getting divorced. What Kurt saw as a friendship, Birddog seemed to see as more of a roadmap.

"So, you want to talk about any of that stuff?"

"Nope."

"You ain't mad?"

"Nope."

"Cause you seemed awfully upset at my place that day."

Kurt could see how Birddog might have come away with that impression. Discovering Birddog eagerly piled atop Katy had triggered some immediate reactions in Kurt. He kicked the door off of Birddog's trailer, knocked over his birdbath, stepped on his cat, and threw his bicycle into a tree. By the time Birddog and Katy righted themselves and came out to see the source of the commotion, Kurt had already jumped on the roof of Katy's car until it was flattened, a ring of shattered glass marking the perimeter of his rage.

"But you're not mad now?"

"She ain't my wife no more. She can screw whoever she pleases."

"You two gonna slow dance or light fireworks?!" came a voice from below.

They both looked into the wheelbarrow. At the shoddily de-signed labels, each screaming the promise of spectacular times at the end of its thin fuse.

"Sorry about your cat."

"It's alright. It was Hattie's anyway. She just never took it with her when she left."

Kurt took a drag from his cigarette and thought of Hattie in high school, with all the kitten stickers on her locker. The only girl he'd ever known to wear her prom dress to her wedding. Frugal, at least. Katy had wanted doves. A dozen white doves to be released the moment they walked out of the church as husband and wife. In the end, she settled for two and a honeymoon in Acapulco. Kurt should have seen it then, when two wasn't enough for her. "You love her?"

"Don't know."

"Yeah. That's as far as I got, too."

"It ain't that hard!" shouted one of the restless. "Just light the fuses!"

Kurt looked over at Birddog and shook his head in exhaustion. "Let's get this over with."

Birddog pulled another rocket from the wheelbarrow, but Kurt took it from him and dropped it back. He had a long pull from his cigarette then flicked it into the pile of fireworks. The paper began to sizzle and Kurt nudged the wheelbarrow down the hill, watching the firebox of amusement barrel toward its audience. It reminded him of Katy. She'd buck and twist and carry on—in bedroom antics that would cloud Kurt's mind for days. His head swam so hard, for so long, he never realized she'd balled him right up to the altar. Later, he remembered his older cousin's observation. "The nutty chicks are the wildest in the sack." He wanted to believe otherwise. But the truth came crashing down around him a few years later in a hail of shrieks and insults and soaring dishes. In a series of red-eyed tempests that were only made bearable by the carnal forgiveness she'd offer up afterward. Until eventually, even that wasn't enough.

"Was that an explosion?"

Kurt glanced at the chaos below. A man had to make his own mistakes. Kurt knew that. Birddog showed him that some men had to make their friends' mistakes, too.

"No, Birddog. You'll know an explosion when you see one."

92

CREATIVE WRITING
James Whorton, Jr.

It's not super easy to become a bank teller, they don't give that job to just any fool, and Ricky applied without hope. At twenty-eight he was still carrying around a large collection of doubts about himself. Something told him his feelings were interesting, that he was a person worth getting to know. Or was he cruel and a whiner? Going back to college was no longer an option, his incompletes having turned to failures. For a while he was writing poems. He posted them online in a poetry forum where people could read and comment. One day he posted a haiku and someone commented, *You would not know a haiku if it slapped you on the buttcheek.* Ricky posted another haiku to show he didn't care, then he rode his bike to the top of a parking garage in downtown Rochester. The top level had no roof, just a low wall around the edge. The bike was a late-eighties Peugeot mountain bike that he had picked up for forty dollars on Craigslist. It was black with orange and yellow decals, sort of cool and weird, kind of heavy, maybe junk. He walked his bike to the edge and looked over. The sidewalk was four levels down. His arms went limp, and his feet were suddenly damp.

Before jumping he checked his phone one last time. "*Welcome to the Rochester Federal Bnank team.*" Sometimes life-saving news comes with a word spelled wrong in it, but it had saved him that night just the same. Now he was a bank teller. He wore clean shirts and hard shoes every day, and he had taught himself to speak in a manner that felt breezy yet professional. He had plans to buy a car. One morning he was working window number two when a man in a dark hoodie stepped up.

"What can I do for you today?" Ricky said.

"Read this." The man pushed a folded sheet of loose-leaf notebook paper across the counter.

His eyes were dull, his beard soiled. He breathed through his mouth, showing small teeth and red, sore-looking gums. All over him the man had a hurt look, like his body hurt but also his brain, like he was irritated and generally bad off. Like someone had injured him a long time ago, and he'd been injured often since, too many times. Most of us bury our pain, it kind of goes along with living in civilization, but this man looked ready to share his pain with Ricky right now.

He shifted in his hoodie, breathing noisily. He squirmed a hand into his hoodie pocket.

Ricky's feet went damp. An idea came to him of how interested certain persons would feel when they learned he had been shot to death in the Monroe Avenue branch of Rochester Federal Bank by a drug-addled unhoused street person. Ricky's life, trivial and storyless up to this point, would have found its crisis and climax. Some who had not thought of him since high school, who had barely noticed him even then, would soon be remembering him on Facebook.

But he was confused. On the paper under his fingers he made out the word "garbage" and the word "grape." What kind of stick-up note was this? And when had he last come across a page of actual human handwriting? In pencil, too.

"Also I need to cash my refund check," the man said. From his hoodie pocket he produced not the cheap chrome-plated revolver that Ricky had imagined but a bent envelope marked "United States Internal Revenue Service."

A new understanding glimmered in Ricky's brain. Seeing he was not about to die, he felt so happy, filled with a greedy love of life. At the same time he noted with dismay that he had already mashed the small panic button that was next to his leg. Most days he ran a finger over it once or twice idly, speculatively, like touching a sore tooth. This time he had mashed the panic button hard. No alarm sounded, but Carole, the branch manager, came speed walking out of her office waving a ghostly white bag. Ricky marveled in soft confusion as Carole dumped his cash drawer into the white bag and zipped it. She slid the bag across the counter to the hoodie man.

"What's this?" the hoodie man said.

"Please take it and go," Carole said. "Nobody's resisting. Take it! Go." She didn't look scared, just bossy and businesslike. The man did what he'd been ordered to do. When he was gone, Carole ran across the lobby, flinging her elbows side to side, and locked the glass doors behind him. Then she ran away from the doors and said "Oh my God" in a voice that sounded like she had swallowed a Kleenex.

Jeannie, the other teller, burst into tears.

Carole ran up to Ricky. "You did the right thing," she said. "You handled it correctly, Ricky! Are you OK?" She snatched up the note from the counter. She read it. "This is not a stick-up note," she said.

Soon the police arrived. A lot of them. Many questions were asked of Ricky. Why would somebody who is robbing a bank also be cashing a check at that bank? Answer, somebody would not. Why, when he knew better, did Ricky stand there saying nothing? Answer, he was uncertain. Uncertain what was happening, or uncertain why he said nothing? Answer, both. It appeared that Ricky was uncertain about a multitude of things. He was awfully slow to call something what it was. "You screwed up," Carole said. Luckily, hoodie man had dropped his IRS check in the parking lot. His name and address were on the check. The police went to his house (he did live in a house), he gave the bag of money back, they gave him back his IRS check. It was a long day and a bad day, and at the end of it Ricky did not work for Rochester Federal Bank anymore.

He pedaled his cool or possibly stupid late-eighties Peugeot mountain bike along Monroe Avenue to downtown, up the river to the Ford Street bridge, down the river to High Falls, and across through a yellow-green mist that climbed off the crashing water. He rode south along St. Paul past the giant Genesee Brewing Company beer tanks and from there to the parking garage, where he pedaled without stopping up the spiral ramp to the roofless fourth level. A pale hazy ring shone around the rising moon. It was beautiful and strange. Why now? A sublime display of the heavens had appeared at a moment when it was useless to Ricky, when Ricky could only be unhappy. Crows screamed, flying west, thousands making their nightly commute to Washington Square Park where their sloppy, berry-colored droppings would stain the sidewalks, the parking meters, and the windshields of cars. Sometimes the city set off cannon sounds to scare them away. But the crows kept coming back, returning from their daily feedings in the suburbs to release upon the city their purple splatter-bombs with little seeds in them.

The world is disorderly and confusing. Then the police arrive, calling everything by name. How do some people know what to call things all the time? Reaching for his phone, Ricky touched the folded paper that had found its way into his pocket after Carole had shoved it into his hand, telling him "This is yours," after telling him "Don't come back," just before she bumped him on his butt with the glass door which she then locked behind him.

He opened the page and studied it as well as he could by the available moonlight. Again he read the lines and they still, to him, made little sense. Why *grape*, why *garbage*? Who proffers a poem to a bank teller? More to the point, why do poems even exist in this baffling world?

Anyway he forgot for the moment about jumping and instead coasted down the long spiral ramp to street level, his life prolonged again by a partly garbled string of words.

MAKING RUINS: Are we what we make?
Mac Walcott

The thick dull blade penetrated the green fender about ten inches from my pelvis. I found it lying in the mud right next to the rear wheel of my old JD 1070 tractor. The broken blade had launched from the shaft of the antique bush hog after I hit a pile of sunken concrete furnace blocks while clearing an overgrown corner of our place. Once the blade had broken off, the imbalanced bush hog started a violent heaving that shut the tractor down, starting the inspection that shivers me each time I remember finding the dead blade. Later in the year, while plowing, I "burned up" that tractor, the mechanic's term for foolishly running it low on coolant till it overheated. The head warped and spewed foul smelling oily steam all over the machine. It sat for many months in a pile of other ruined tractors till someone bought it for parts.

The furnace blocks were left over from a forgotten fire pit I had built for the kids fifteen years ago. I hauled them to Alabama thirty-two years before, after pilfering them from an old New Orleans printing plant that was being consumed by nature. They sat patiently for many years as I imagined grand plans of how they would be used. The causing of my near death was not in these plans, but ruins have a way of stinging us when we forget about them.

When I was around nine or ten, I remember telling my mother on several occasions that I wanted to "make something"; nothing in particular, just the urge to make. In becoming an architect, and practicing at it for almost forty years now, I have been deeply immersed in the making of many things and places, some beautiful, some awful. In seeing some of these made structures now begin to deteriorate, or even be demolished, I'm pushed into a world that is more in sync with the world we all see in our own communities, a world in which most everything is headed to ruins, the only way that our physical world can go. This journey to near perdition is unrelenting, and we stumble on many routes to get there, each with diabolical contradictions.

Our Faiths teach us about an infinite world that is constantly ending and being reborn, with new life built on the remains and memories of the old. In the summer of 2006, our son and his high school buddies built a boardwalk through our swamp to a small pond. We then cleverly prefabricated the walls and roof framing for a future Thoreau-inspired screen house at the end of the boardwalk. When we finished erecting the framing pieces, he snidely commented "this will make great ruins someday." He spoke as any sixteen-year-old, unsure of what he should believe in, but sure he needed to say something. It was a stinging and knowing remark that was proven true fourteen years later when the whole unfinished mess of treated wood collapsed upon itself into the muck after Hurricane Sally. I have been down there once since and may never go again. My faith is at the bottom of that folly for now, but will emerge again one day, as indomitable as the hidden furnace blocks that broke the bush hog.

Our Economies teach us that "creative destruction" is necessary for the constant re-creation of the artifacts we build, all for the promised 'greater good' of our communities. My grandfather built a sixty-year business from scratch around the ginning, de-linting and sale of certified cotton seed in the Mississippi Delta. I remember visiting my father at work there as a child and seeing two city blocks of old and imposing warehouse buildings that fronted the downtown railroad tracks. After college, I remember the anguish in my father as he supervised the salvage workers tearing down these buildings for scrap metal to pay off the bankrupt back-rent owed to the railroad.

Those two city blocks on the railroad frontage are still barren, forty years later.

Our Sciences teach us to believe in certainties, that concepts such as "the edge of the universe" or "settled science" should be easy to comprehend. In April of this year, a captain ran his boat full speed into our dock at nine p.m. on a Sunday night. He claimed to be following the "bread crumb" tracks on his new satellite GPS. It was high tide, and the vessel with its six passengers and 220 hp projected itself completely onto our dock and partly through the roof above. Within moments of the allision, the captain's cell phone automatically notified his daughter on land, and within thirty minutes she knocked on our door. We went into the darkness together to find her bloodied parents waiting patiently on their boat, in our rafters. All six survived and our dock became an instant ruin, joining the ranks of the many slouching and decrepit docks on our river that are succumbing to the inevitable downward flow of our water and our gravity, all as certain as the signals on his GPS that night.

Our Warriors teach us that the clarifying necessity of conflict will always be with us. Each day now, we watch the precise images of the beautifully significant elements of Ukrainian communities being pounded into more rubble, a first layer of the type of rubble that undermines the layered Tels of the ancient cities of the Middle East. These layers of rubble are the only way our warriors know how to build. Are we learning to build our communities in the same manner?

Our Representatives teach us that winners *must* take all, and that one vote over fifty percent is all that is necessary to make a modern consensus. Many years ago, our local newspaper had a daily front page column called "Sound Off," in which citizens could vent their feelings anonymously. It was heavily curated and mostly contained *ad hominem* attacks on various personalities in the news that day. The newspaper, like so many others, has now gone to ruin, but its legacy of anonymous attacks has been industrialized and normalized by its high-tech successors. As we wade into our morning reads today, we dodge the digital debris of the slandered and ruined souls that once wanted to be part of our communities. Are these vanquished souls being prepared to become another layer of rubble under another new meta city, or will they be rejuvenated and offer us the hope that nourishes all communities?

I am haunted and enthralled by ruins, both made and imagined, and look for the day when our ruins can make us whole—a day when the duels between our entropy and our hubris will be melded back into the ruins of Eden, where they belong.

It will be a day well made.

From *SECOND SLUTHOOD*
R.P. Saffire

I got married the first time right out of high school in 1971—
because it was to be my Great Escape. Also because my mother,
Bizarro Harriet, wanted me to be the Bride of the Universe. Just the
thing to show all her country club friends that she could rise to their
occasion and plan a day any Emily Post zombie would pronounce a
success. My father, Bizarro Ozzy, went along to get along.

The boyfriend, a quiet, laid-back football player to whom
my precious virginity was given, (not in a bedroom bed—how many
teenage de-flowerings are conducted on an actual mattress?—but
on a horse blanket in the galvanized steel bed of a royal blue Ford
pickup truck), was the love of my life. What did I know? I wanted
out of Bizarro world. I was young, I had a mother who was dying to
throw a wedding, and I had a boyfriend who was so blown away by
a semblance of real sex that he would do anything to hang on to a
willing partner. That poor, horny halfback from my eleventh grade
government class, a Testosterone Drone who passed me notes during
anti-communism reel-to-reels. I played it coy for a while, then the
Cold War escalated as we began to date, building to a summit of
heat, when, at last, I shed the Bobbie Brooks dress, and the heels of
my Weejuns pounded the Ford tailgate like an angry Khrushchev. We
were hooked on lust.

Which brings me to the wedding. As I said before, my
nut-covered cheese ball of a mother was tickled senseless, flinging
herself into the planning, the selection of the sterling, the winnowing
of the Wedgewood. I yielded to her; she seemed to be having a grand
time with it, the most fun I had ever witnessed her enjoying. Anyway,
I was already enough of a budding feminist to see it as an archaic
little minuet, the purpose of which was to transfer ownership of the
non-existent maidenhead from the father to the husband.

But as the day of *petite forts* and the passing of the property
unfolded, it dawned on me that I was nothing more than an actor on
an elaborate stage, adoring fans flinging rice and rose petals, reviews

100

due out in Sunday's society section of the *Mobile Press Register*. And my co-star was not even my soon-to-be spouse; it was my mother. She was beaming, basking in the glow of the footlights. By the time the reception was in full swing, a veritable tsunami of disgust rolled over me, washing up the primal urge to flee the scene, take a do-over, and elope with my true love.

Which he wasn't. My true love, that is. He did have a name, which I have not yet mentioned, a conscious device intended to symbolize his presence as a prop in the pageant. We had not spent much time conversing, sharing life goals, swapping opinions or philosophies or desires (or lack thereof) for offspring.

My dear husband's name was "Doodoo."

Okay, it was a nickname. All the jocks had nicknames; it was some kind of requirement. His real name was *Daniel*. I wished the preacher had used his nickname in the nuptials: "Do you, Doodoo, take" etc. It would have revealed the ceremony for what it was: manure. Doodoo and I found ourselves wedded strangers for whom the novelty of sex wore off post haste, for whom the bell tolled with certainty. The reality of morning breath, dirty underwear, bodily functions, and a mother-in-law who had instilled in her only son a learned helplessness that made a toddler look self-sufficient ensured that it was annulled in well under three months.

I flung myself into college, that academic collage of high ideas, illegal substances, and random sexual encounters. Without the first notion of pedigree, I treated the institution as a Whitman's Sampler of disciplines, psychology my first nibble. I would be renowned as a female B.F. Skinner, navigating the maze-like minds of my fellows. Or I would come up with my own theories about the behavings of the brain, winning prizes, winnowing my way up the Hierarchy of my Needs. But I could not pass statistics; after failing for the third time, I moved on. (But not before getting *id*-ish with a grad assistant who taught me the value of delayed gratification. What a gynecological gestalt! With Doodoo it had been all about frantic friction; the world was now my Carnal Oyster, over which I salivated with Pavlovian glee.)

My love of semi-precious stones led me to geology, but

precious little time was spent discussing gems. It was all about crusts, rocks and such; I again moved on. (But not before my lab partner fractured another barrier to my sexual elation, excavating and spelunking his way to my Pacific rim. Maybe it was the discussions of the hardness of specimens, cleavage, rings of fire, erupting volcanoes, shuddering earthquakes. That particular department was simply bathed in heat, steam, fissures, rumblings, boilings, and spewing, glowing lava flows; "Stoney" and I utilized lab tables, broom closets, and empty classrooms and offices, swept up by tidal surges of lust born of deep oceanic quiverings building into furious, demanding explosions. "Rocks" took on a whole new meaning for me.)

By now I was sporting hairy underarms, bouncing breasts, and eschewing make-up: the hippie chic style of the day. I dabbled in the psychedelic realm, Mary Jane an occasional acquaintance, but my chemical inclination tended toward the vine. And, surprise-surprise, I was attracted to the one male who stood out as completely different from the potheads: a frat boy named Bobby. Whom I married.

It was a doomed union, of course.

And yes, it was a "mixed" marriage. He was a wholesome, Pat-Boone-ish (though he, like my father, could damn sure put away some PBR) Kappa Alpha. I was a wild, Janis Jopliny GDI, having much earlier in college life briefly put my toe in Greek waters at the urging of Bizarro Harriet.

"It's all about making useful social connections," my socially inappropriate *mater* had advised.

"You know I am not a joiner of things."

"Yes, alas," she sighed, martyred at the holy blissful shrine of her Disappointment In Me.

"Please don't do that."

"Prithee, what?"

"Make me feel guilty."

She gave me her eyes-brimming-with-tears look. "If the guilt fits."

So I became a Chi Omega during my freshman year, and for exactly seven months was immersed in everything Chi-O, from propagandizement in pledge world to the official acceptance to songs, rituals, candles, and frat boys, whom I found too familiar, too home-townish, when I had a yen for the exotic. This was about the time I began to size up the geology department, so I was already riled, steeped in the cyclic heat of the estrul ether. Those frat boys just were not ramping up the heat, determined as they were to impress one another with their ability to win drinking games. I began to skip the Greek parties in favor of more artistic groups, began to gain a little knowledge of myself, began to feel creative stirrings within my soon-to-be unbound bosom.

As I came into my own, sprouting golden hairs upon my tanned (via basting in Johnson's Baby Oil) legs; casting off my padded and be-hooked Maidenform brassiere, my sisters of the sorority became sore confounded. At first they let out little bleats of disapproval.

"Ruby Pearl, you're starting to look like one of those hippie people." Sissy Somebody said.

"Must you label others?" I replied, bosoms bobbing beneath my "Chi Omega" t-shirt.

"There *have* to be labels," SS said, going through a list of Pan Hellenic Council groups and their respective traits—such as which sorority was known for serious, brainy girls, which for unattractive and downright ugly "dogs," which for party girls and sluts, always winding up with, "but the Chi-Os are known for being the best looking."

"Have you not read *The Feminine Mystique?*" I retorted.

Blank stares.

They finally grew desperate enough to stage something like an intervention, gathering in my dorm room, speaking in hushed tones, wearing looks of exaggerated concern.

"We love you," Buffy Somebody said in that sweet, fake-Christian tone so rampant in the South. "We're your sisters."

Now, I am not one who is fond of being gushed over, told I am loved, or given advice—particularly from fake Christians, and especially when I have not sought said advice. What was the source of all the concern? After much and mighty buildup, it came out:

Not only did they object to the body hair, I was dating "hippie guys" and "everybody knows that Chi Omegas go out with Kappa Sigmas—on this campus anyway."

"The least you could do," Tootie Somebody sighed, "is date a few Greeks."

I left their ranks. That day.

STAR CAPTAIN & THE END TIMES
Karen Spears Zacharias

The city park was desolate, isolated, the kind of place one would expect to meet up with rabid demon dogs or worse, the Walking Dead. My friend had driven me to the Alabama knoll where Star Captain told me to be. My buddy, feeling uneasy about my joining some man I'd never met before, suggested I might want to pick a more public spot.

Star Captain didn't seem like the sort of fellow who was amenable to last minute changes. I was already worried that *he* might cancel the meeting, given that Mercury was being so moody and all. I'd assured my friend that I was a big girl, that I'd be fine, that I did this sort of thing all the time. As soon as I saw the park, I changed my mind. It looked exactly like the sort of place where Ted Bundy and Charles Manson might meet to play checkers, discuss brands of knives and old girlfriends.

I called Star Captain, told him I couldn't meet there. "The bugs will eat me up." It's true. Skeeters, ticks and fleas will hunt me down for a sip of my blood. Vampires would kill for it.

"Too much banana oil," Star Captain said, as if that was the most sensible thing in the world.

"What?"

"You eat too many bananas. That's why the bugs bite you."

"Uh, okay." I tried my darndest to recall the last time I'd eaten a banana.

Star Captain agreed to meet at Wendy's instead. The girl at the counter wore a t-shirt with the verse Jeremiah 29:11 in bold ink: "For I know the plans I have for you, declares the Lord, plans to prosper you and not to harm you, plans to give you hope and a future."

Star Captain arrived: black pants, black vest, black shoes, black cap with "Atmospheres" stitched across the front. He's small of bone and frame, might tip the scales at 140 pounds. Gray stubble roughs up his otherwise translucent skin. The mark of someone who spends a lot of time indoors. There's gentleness to his hazel eyes, the way they turn down at the corners when he's studying on something, the animated wide-eyed wonder of some discovery he shares. You can see the boy behind the man in Star Captain's eyes.

The white vinyl notebook he carries is thick with astrological charts he's sketched. "We are going to have a total economic collapse," Star Captain says, opening it. "I've been doing this for 40 years. See?" He turns to a chart that looks much like a Spiro-graph drawing. Across the top in small but readable print is a date: Feb. 3rd, 1970. Beneath it, the event: Pan Am Crash. "Remember the day the Twin Towers came down? Saturn and Pluto were in direct dead opposition."

He pulls another chart from his folder. "Now we have a hard, five-planet square of opposition. Come August all hell is going to break loose."

"This August?"

"Yes. We're in a Mercury retrograde."

I nod, though I'm not sure what retrograde means. It sounds bad, and in my experience as a writer if a word is guttural when pronounced, you can bet that somewhere the angels are singing *Bad Moon Rising*, which if you think about it is the perfect theme song for the Book of Revelation: *I know the end is coming soon.*

Call it an Astrological Apocalypse if you like.

"Everything is being held up, delayed. That's especially true for publishing. Mercury controls all our communication. Expect to be frustrated." Star Captain doles out warnings like a Coney Island vendor passing out quarters. He's on full alert these days. "Earthquakes, volcanic activity are going to increase, co-relating to Revelation, the Bible. The signs of the planets, moon and stars are going into alignment with Scriptures."

He's been having dreams, of people in a panic.

And that's not all.

Thirty days before 9-11 he was visited by "a big-winged creature." A Phoenix bird. "At my front door."

Native Americans consider it a great blessing when the Eagle swoops down to visit them, a sign from the Great Father. But you don't want the Phoenix to come a-knocking. He took the creature's appearance as a warning.

106

Some might consider Star Captain left of plumb, one pickle shy. Perhaps. Maybe he's just born to the wrong age. There's a lot unreasonable about this age of reason in which we live. The more civilized we've become the less civilized we act. Maybe indigenous tribes who still pay attention to the stars have something in common with Star Captain. Maybe they have insights the rest of us lack.

Star Captain is preparing for the coming collapse. He's got oil lanterns, glo-lights, cases of Tang, bags of rice, cans of chicken, guns and ammo.

"Enough to take care of myself."

Not standing on a street corner, preaching, he does what he can to warn those within his circle. Sometimes they heed his advice. Sometimes they don't.

"Not a damn thing I can do about it," he says. "People have closed minds, unblinkered thinking."

That's their problem, not his, unmotivated by fear.

"I'm not scared of death." He believes he will rise again, in some form or another. "We have the choice to either stay earthbound when we die or head toward the light."

He was raised up Baptist, believes in eternal damnation for rapists, murderers, homicidal maniacs and such. "They will have their Waterloo," he says. But he parted ways with the Baptists on March 1, 1970. He has an uncanny knack for remembering dates, a helpful trait for those who plan their lives according to complicated equations. He started studying astrology, which a friend suggested. As he told me about it my cell phone rang, one of my three daughters. "I'll call you back. I'm in the middle of an interview."

"She's forty."

"What?"

"Your daughter — she's forty."

He's right. She is.

It's kind of whoo-hoo creepy, but I believe Star Captain has the gift of knowing things, like my daughter's age. He tells me more about myself, mostly true.

He's a survivalist if he's anything, but don't discount him as a prophet. His primary concern is that of any good Boy Scout – Be prepared. "There is nothing we can do to alter the course of events to come. All we can do is prepare."

He's bright enough to know that his warnings are falling on deaf ears. "People are heedless, ignorant. It's hard when you see so much, feel so much, but nobody else can understand. It's not an easy life."

He points again to his dotted chart. "It's going to get real, real, real bad."

People get ready, he urges.

A week later I was driving along Interstate 10. My phone rang, Star Captain calling.

"You know how I get impressions about things?" not even saying hello, his voice unmistakable, like Anderson Cooper's or Whoopi Goldberg's.

"Yeah." I still haven't figured out if he suffers from delusions or if he bubbles right below the surface, seeing two worlds simultaneously.

"I got this impression a little while ago about you, thought I better call, make sure you're okay."

I was stunned speechless.

"Get yourself a manual typewriter," Star Captain said. "Stock up on paper and ribbon."

I haven't typed on a manual typewriter since Billy Carter strolled the streets of Plains, Georgia, acting like he didn't know his brother Jimmy. I've lived long enough that the tools of my youth are now flea market treasures. Writing is a hard enough task without having to fool with liquid White-Out, but I didn't want to get into all that.

"Why do I need a typewriter? If the world is coming to an end soon, why bother writing?" I wasn't trying to be rude; it's a reasonable question. If you aren't doing the thing you'd be doing if this was your last week on earth maybe you ought to be doing some other thing. Writing is that thing for me. But I wasn't expecting the answer Star Captain gave me.

"Because we need your voice."

"Even if the world is ending?"

"Especially then."

Star Captain had another word of caution for me that might

have creeped me out if I were superstitious. "You need to hurry and get home as quickly as possible."

I told Star Captain that it was by no means going to be a quick trip. I had over 2,400 miles to drive.

"Are you driving alone?"

"Yes."

"Uh-oh. Uh-oh."

It's unsettling whenever Star Captain gets the Uh-ohs.

"What?" I asked.

"Nothing. You just need to get home as quickly as possible. Be careful, don't stop to talk to strangers along the way. Keep to yourself."

I didn't bother asking if that meant I wasn't supposed to talk to strangers like him. And what? Miss a good story?

While I appreciated Star Captain's concern, if the End Times is indeed upon us, I want to be able to speak of my life's misadventures the way my Mama does.

"Liked to have died" is Mama's favorite phrase. She says it all the time. When she goes to Wal-Mart and can't find the milk aisle she says, "I liked to have died before I found that cooler." When she goes to Les Schwab to get her tires rotated for spring, she says, "The line was so long I liked to have died." When she works in the yard all day long, Mama says, "It's so hot I liked to have died."

On the off chance I'm raptured along some backwoods road in South Alabama one fine day, just know I liked to have died on my way to Gloryland.

ME vs. SLUGS: PANDEMIC EDITION
Beth Ann Fennelly

When the terrible virus was unleashed and our lives screeched to a halt, I planted a garden. My first. I tended it zealously, with the darting eyes of a suicide bomber. This was March, April, May, the world hijacked by hysteria. I could have watered my garden with tears after returning from the store rumored to have toilet paper, after scrubbing my hands and changing my clothes and scrubbing my hands and disinfecting every sack of off-brand rice, every dented can of beans.

So, the garden. I would grow our groceries. I would knit a chlorophyll blanket around my family: my industry, their immunity.

At first, it worked. Everything grows in Mississippi, even for a "gardener" Googling "how to plant a seed." In a Mississippi minute, things were sprouting, burgeoning, prospering: #winning.

Until the day my frothy cilantro fronds went missing; only their naked flagpoles remained, resembling chives. The next day, no poles. And, for that matter, no chives. My fennel (yes, I'd grown it solely for the name) was depilated. My dill, dead-headed. What invisible blight was this? My garden was syruped in sunshine, watered daily, and mulched to keep my sproutlings moist.

Slugs, said Google. Slugs shimmy from under the mulch at night. They munch until dawn, then slime back under the mulch, engage in some hermaphroditic kink, then squirt out thirty eggs. And you know what happens to the eggs: everything grows in Mississippi.

Beer, said Google, a plate of beer is the answer. I poured a can into a Frisbee, placed the shallow grave in the garden, set my alarm for 4:30 am. With my phone flashlight I returned. Six or seven gray bloated bodies lolled in their Bud Light Jacuzzi. But angling my phone I could see other slugs still chomping. Not thirty, but thirty times thirty times thirty, the flagstones glistening with their calligraphy, the screen door snotty with secretions. I donned my gardening gloves like a knight would his gauntlets, plucked a fat slug from a leaf of butter crunch, and chucked it into the grass. But it was probably already U-turning to resume its salad course. I plucked another, gritted my molars, and squished. Enough: I didn't have the stomach for it.

Two-thirds of my children accepted the bribe, a dime a slug, thrilled to be out past bedtime and armed with flashlights. The nine-year-old earned $2.60, the fourteen-year-old $4.10. But the next night they quit after only a buck a piece. "There aren't any more," they claimed the third night. But, oh, the slugs were there. I could feel them crawling in the tender hollow at the back of my neck.

I foraged deeper into Google, which now said beer was not the answer; instead, wait for midnight, make a pail of suds, drop the slugs in. They'd die beneath the bubbles, and I wouldn't have to watch or assist.

Google was right about the soapy water, but beer was still the answer. I drank it steadily, girding for battle. Then I rampaged through my garden until every last slug had been dunked. The next day, I made my husband empty the sluggish pail. Game over.

Months later, when things were still bad, but better, when we understood how the virus spread, and learned to wear masks, and thought we might survive, my fourteen-year-old mentioned the night of my slug fest, mentioned hearing me in the garden.

"Oh, really?" I asked uneasily.

"Yeah," he said. "I woke up, and I could hear you cursing."

"Cursing?"

"Yeah."

It remains to be seen how historians will contextualize this long dark pall of pandemic, the fraying of global mental health, the toll on our children's futures. And that official reckoning will overlap with our private reckonings, the large suffering as well as the smaller stories, the cringe-worthy, told for a laugh. Perhaps at a dinner party, say, people offering up their personal pandemic low. I won't have to scramble for mine. That night, which should have rightfully slipped into oblivion, is now freshly imagined from the point of view of my son, lying in his bed, in the dark, listening to his drunkish mother marauding in the Mississippi night.

"You kept calling them"—he broke off—"Can I say the word? Without getting in trouble?"

I nodded.

"—Assholes. You'd shout at each slug, before dropping it in the pail, 'You're a little asshole.'"

I closed my eyes in a slow blink.

"And—" he continued.

"Yeah?"

"Sometimes you'd laugh."

WHISKEY BLUES
Rick Bragg

My first lesson on brown whiskey came forty years ago, in a time of bad sideburns and slick leisure suits and eight track troubadours. I seem to remember Tanya Tucker calling to me from the dashboard, and the Alabama sun burning through the open window of my metalflake-brown Pontiac Grand Prix. I was a newspaper guy then, on my way to a story I can no longer recall. The Pontiac was bad to run hot, but I made it all the way to the middle of nowhere before it finally blew a radiator hose and died in the ditch. I stepped out into a green-gray cloud of scalding steam, cursing all the Pontiacs that Michigan ever made.

I looked north, then south. Nothing. The closest garage or parts house was twenty miles away, and I couldn't remember the last farmhouse or mobile home I had seen. I waited twenty minutes before I saw a car, then, five minutes later, another; they didn't even slow down. I threw my necktie into the back seat – I did not want to die in a clip-on – and started walking. The asphalt shimmered in front of me, bottle caps tamped down into the soft tar.

I didn't really notice the truck, an ancient Ford, till it rolled up beside me. An old man in overalls and a begrimed undershirt, one knobby elbow out the window, looked me up and down.

I was a country boy, myself, or at least I had been. Hard to tell, I guess, in that Banlon shirt that was smoldering across my back.

"Whar's yore hat?" was all he said, like I was an imbecile left to wander in the weeds.

I crawled into the cab. It smelled of burnt motor oil and gasoline and old beer. I knew it would.

"Thar's a parts house in Heflin," he said. He didn't even consider driving to a house and calling a tow truck. Any fool could change a radiator hose.

"Got any water?" I asked, and he just shook his head and handed me a pint bottle of whiskey, the kind that bootleggers sell in every dry county in the world.

"I better not," I said. "I'm workin'."

He just looked all around us, at the wide-open, broad, green nothing. If ever there was a land made for secrets, it was Clay County, Alabama.

I unscrewed the cap and took a slash…

I still can't really describe it, how it seared and abraded my throat. I imagined broken glass, in a puddle of burning gasoline.

AAAARRRRGGGHHHH, my mind screamed.

But I did not cough and sputter, like they do in the movies. Steam did not pour from my ears, like in the cartoons. I did not pray to Jesus. Back then, young men did not act a fool in front of their elders.

I just thanked him, hoarsely, and wiped away a tear.

He took a slash himself, and, as the miles passed beneath us, poured out his wisdom on inexpensive alcohol.

"See, son, your cheap likker won't hurt a man's insides, because it's weaker than that fancy whiskey, like that Jack Daniels, or that Kentucky bourbon," he said. "That'll burn a hole right through you."

If cheap liquor would kill a man, he said, there wouldn't be any poor men left to walk on God's green earth. It would just be Lutherans and teetotalers and rich men, and what a sorry place that would be.

That logic did not sound precisely right to me, but I nodded, anyway. I'd only had three swallows, and I was already pretty well drunk, for daytime.

I told him the truth; I never had tasted any good liquor.

He told me, in all his long life, he never had, either.

*

Twenty years later, I sat at a table in midtown Manhattan with a small gathering of writers and editors, ex-patriated Southerners who followed their dreams and ambitions to West 42nd Street, Broadway, and Park Avenue; if ever there had been a caucus of people who knew their brown liquor, this was it. Expensive bottles gleamed behind the bar, as waiters brought out some of the finest alcohol Kentucky and

Tennessee ever made. "Rich folks' likker," my uncles would have called it, but they would have said it with respect. There were bottles behind that bar, gleaming amber and gold, that cost more than my Grand Prix.

Someone passed me a glass, and I took a gentlemanly sip. *AAARRRRRRGGGGHHHH*, my mind screamed.

And right then, I knew. I could barely tell the difference between a $200 bottle of brown liquor in an overpriced midtown restaurant and a $2 snort from an old man's traveling whiskey on the road to Lineville.

There was just something missing in me, something that should have been inherent. I had grown into a man believing that there were just some things a man needed to know, no matter what class he was born to, things like fishing lures, and good shotguns, and how to sharpen a knife. And a man should know brown liquor, from the bar brands in a honkytonk to the bottle gathering dust in a rich man's will and testament.

I was *born* to know it; my grandpa made corn whiskey in the deep hollers of the mountain South, and did time in Atlanta when the federals ran him down on a pulpwood road. My kin drank. Whiskey was as essential as air. Sobriety, we truly believed, was a rock we crawled upon only to die.

I remember seeing my Uncle Jimbo stand on a riverbank with a pint of Tennessee whiskey in his fist, remember seeing him turn it up till it was all gone, remember the look of wonder on his face, like he had discovered something in the bottom of that thin, flat bottle that no one had ever experienced before.

And he would make a sound, a sound that was part exultation, part scream.

Now I know it was just a rebel yell.

If it was just fair whiskey, he would bait his hook, find a tree to lean against, and fall asleep.

If it was good whiskey, he would do a little buck dance by the water's edge, tell lies till he was out of breath, and sing every song Jimmie Rodgers ever made.

I, of all people, should have the gift.

I'm a *writer*, for God's sake.

I'm a *Southern* writer.

Find a sober one.

Go ahead.

Try.

I always understood the escape that brown liquor could bring. It provided a rare kind of peace of mind, a cloudy good will. Once, in a bar in Uptown New Orleans, I toasted the LSU Tigers. I *hate* the LSU Tigers.

But if a man can't really tell the difference between rough and smooth, between good and bad, then he was a Philistine. It was just anesthesia. I drank less and less. The myth of fine alcohol was just that: myth.

Yet, even when I *confessed*, when I told people of my ignorance, they seemed not to hear. Nice people kept pouring fancy liquor down me, believing I had some kind of divining rod in my bones. I had written books about whiskey men, hadn't I? I tried to tell them I didn't drink much, but people still did it, engaging me on caramel coloring and smoky hints and charred barrels, while lamenting the tragic fire in Kentucky that consumed a treasure trove of Pappy Van Winkle. I thought Pappy Van Winkle was a nursery rhyme.

Somehow, bizarrely, I even developed a reputation for the drinking I did not do.

"Is poor ol' Rick still having trouble with the bottle?" someone would say.

"He can't help it, bless his heart," someone would answer. "You know, his people was always that way."

I know this because another well-meaning soul would report what they had said, and then pat me on the arm. The beautiful thing about Southerners is how happy they are to tell you all the evil things that other people say about you.

It was even said that I had a phantom bottle of aged whiskey in my desk drawer, the way old newspapermen and authors used to do. I did have an ancient, gummy peppermint, and a three-year-old pouch of Delta Airline peanuts.

I found it easier, in time, to just go along with it all. It made me picturesque. I always wanted to be picturesque.

I accepted glass after glass, joining in conversations on Gentleman Jack or Jim Beam Black, on the differences between the craftsmen of Kentucky bourbon and Tennessee whiskey, between Scotch and Irish, blended and single malt …and on and on. But even as I got older, it all still tasted alike, all tasted harsh; even the smoothest brown whiskey tasted like green persimmons to me.

And I'd just nod and say, "Man, that's *smoooooooth.*"

No one ever seemed to notice that, when I got up from the table, the glass was still mostly full. I have poured good whiskey on the sand. I have, literally, watered the plants in restaurants.

Someone told me, a while back, they had heard I had *finally* quit drinking. I sure was glad to hear that.

But then I heard I had backslid and was back in my cups, again. That's the way it is with imaginary whiskey. Once it gets its imaginary claws in you, it's almost impossible to imaginarily yank that imaginary monkey off your back.

*

Maybe, I wondered, if I was not destined to like brown liquor? Maybe, as strange as it might seem, I was a martini man.

Nope. Vermouth reminded me of the time I accidentally ate a Wet Nap at the Kentucky Fried Chicken in Sylacauga.

I was relieved to learn this. Martini drinkers all seemed like people I would like to punch in the snoot.

It was the same with all other cocktails. Designer vodka tasted like paint thinner; fine, dry gin tasted medicinal. Unless you were in the jungle, being carried off by mosquitoes and malaria, there just didn't seem to be any point. High-end tequila tasted like soap. Sherry tasted like cough drops.

I had a Manhattan once. I do not possess the words. Goat sputum, maybe.

I hoped, sincerely, it would be different with rum; I had, after all, spent much of my writing life in the tropics. In places like Haiti, Miami, and New Orleans. Maybe this was the brown liquor I was meant to drink, and love. Pirates drank rum. Revolutions were fueled by it.

Nada. I could not differentiate a $500 bottle of rum, distilled in the bloody heart of a revolution and smuggled out of the country on the last plane out, from the rum I had inside a plastic pirate's head on spring break 1977 in Panama City Beach.

I had, just once, an inkling of the devotion some drinkers had for brown liquor. Haiti distills a rum called Barbancourt. In it, you can smell the charcoal fires that people use to cook their meals, taste the raw sugarcane. The wet air is thick with ghosts there. You can taste them in it, too.

I watched Democracy break out over a glass of it, sitting in a Petionville bar as, outside, someone threw rocks against the wall. And I tasted, ever so quick, the spirit of the place. And then it was gone.

*

Obviously, I was defective. But in time, as pretension of any kind began to matter less and less to me, I came to wonder if perhaps I was fine, and the rest of the entire, liquor-sipping world was putting me on.

I went to a bourbon tasting at one writing event, just to see if one of those experts would actually use the words "fruity bouquet." No one did, but I heard "essence of oak" and "hints of vanilla" a lot.

If brown liquor was so nuanced, I reasoned, why did many people consume it in something called "shots." Gunslingers, hard-boiled gumshoes, their flinty-eyed molls, clinch-jawed Marines, all "knocked back" their liquor almost contemptuously. It did not even register on their palate before it was in their bloodstream. Only the rich folks had time to sip, and speculate.

I remember a drinking night with my lifelong friend Greg Garrison and some other buddies in a Birmingham bar, in the 1980s. He did five shots of Wild Turkey and accused the waitress of serving him watered-down booze.

"Miss? Miss?" he said, "I think this whitsey is defective."

Now *that* is a connoisseur.

Now I am old and no longer care, but I am forced to admit that, in my lifetime, brown liquor was the conspirator in just about everything I wrote. I remember drinking rum with a man accused of blowing a jetliner from the sky in his private war against Fidel Castro, because politics should only be discussed while drinking, he said, and only in Spanish. I remember sipping whiskey in a bar in New Orleans, watching a woman dance like a snake across the floor; I am pretty sure she was the devil. I remember riding my motorcycle to a white-sand beach on the Coosa River with a Tupperware jug of pre-mixed Jack-and-Coke, remember lying in the hot sun amid a bunch of backsliding Baptists, thinking life would never be so good again. I remember a gagging sip of illegal, forbidden whiskey on a rooftop in Peshawar, Pakistan, and a strong, long pull of bourbon smuggled into the Fox Theater in Atlanta, as Tom Petty sang me to sleep. I remember drinking with freedom fighters, and football coaches, and my father, but that was just in a dream. I even drank Southern Comfort once with Gennifer Flowers, and then she sang me a song; by God, top that.

And once, on a long afternoon in the Mississippi Delta, I drank rot-gut whiskey with a notorious bluesman named T. Model Ford. He kept his whiskey behind the seat of his truck, next to his .38. I asked him, blearily, how many men he had killed.

"Does it count," he said, "if I run over 'em with my Pontiac?"

The liquor runs through it all.

Liquor, and Pontiacs.

I wonder, sometimes, what happened to that old man in Clay County. I'd like to tell him what became of me.

He would probably just unscrew the cap on that bad whiskey, and ask me if, in my world travels, I ever found me a hat.

EVERYONE SAID NOTHING
George Singleton

Looking back, it might not have been such a swift idea, luring would-be burglars onto the property and shooting off their kneecaps with vintage .22 rifles. It had come to that, though. You can't expect normal loving newlyweds, prone to weekend shenanigans, to sit home staring at one-hour melodramas neither of them related to. It's not like we fought big city problems. We hadn't spent time in hospitals. After the movie house shut down and after they made cruising back and forth from Wal-Mart to the Sonic a misdemeanor, we both thought, Well, this town sucks officially. I should say "Wal-Mart parking lot" and "Sonic Drive-Thru parking lot," seeing as both those places folded, as had the three or four locally-owned diners from our childhoods. As had the putt-putt place, bowling alley, pool hall, one bar that had pinball machines, Buck's Wild Petting Zoo, the bar with a Ms. Pac-Man game, and Piedmont Statuary. Everything either moved or floundered. We could've joined one of about eighty-seven churches where congregants praised Jesus for all His bountiful gifts, but that wasn't our style. What bountiful gifts? I said to Nita most nights. She'd go, What even *plain* gifts? We still had the switch yard south of town, sure, but you had to sit on a bluff so far away sometimes two freight train cars clanking together couldn't be heard until about the time you got up to leave.

Anyway, we still got the newspaper. I don't know if I thought this up all by myself or saw something on the local news warning about vacation season, but I thought it might be worthwhile to scatter six folded newspapers, still in plastic weather-protective sleeves, there at the end of our fish hook-shaped driveway. Nita came up with shoving catalogs, flyers, and bills we didn't care about into the mailbox, stuffed, the little door open.

"People see gathering papers and uncollected mail, they figure nobody's home. Nobody home? Good time to break in and steal the silverware and whatnot," I said. "You and I can hide behind the lattice, nights, then aim low. I don't want to kill anyone."

Nita didn't disapprove or protest. Like I said, we'd gotten bored. We figured some of these goddamn idiots who thought the new president could really create jobs for them—jobs meant solely for ninth-grade educated skill-less illiterates—might think it now necessary to break in houses, steal silver, a coin collection or two, maybe our microwave.

I probably don't need to point out that two pawn shops remained in business and prospered. We had pawn shops, but they weren't much to look at after dark on weekend nights.

"We'll be doing good," Nita said. "Next time they go limping into a voting booth still unemployed, they'll think about how they needed health insurance after all."

We made martinis at first, but it affected my aim and I hit two different would-be burglars collarbone high, then elbow, that first week, with my .22 I'd had since squirrel hunting days. We switched over to Manhattans, like that would help. It's funny—everyone said nothing after getting grazed. Nita and I'd see a man, or two men walking together, sneaking up the driveway. She and I didn't go, "Here they come," or "Remember—patella," or "Isn't that the old movie house manager?"

And the burglars kept quiet. Even after getting shot, they'd just turn around dragging one leg behind. We had a lot of blood on our pea gravel that spring. I went and washed it up, then took a rake and shovel trying to turn the evidence over. The last thing we needed was for Google Earth to snapshot our house from outer space, showing a red driveway.

We didn't even have a hospital, just one of those Urgent Care facilities with banking hours. I don't know if our trespassers drove twenty miles to the closest emergency room, or if they found their ways to various trailers and clapboard-sided houses, extracted bullets with needle-nosed pliers, then duct taped their kneecaps on straight.

So that was March through June, pretty much. Nita and I made a living, both of us, buying old manual typewriters from our community—Royals, Underwoods, Remingtons, the occasional infrequent Olivetti—by the pound, or for five bucks each at most. We took the keys off and sold them to a jewelry designer up in Asheville. This wasn't a difficult task. Before the town officially imploded, pre-computer-using cotton mills dissolved in the mid-eighties. Hell, my wife and I own a large collection of slide rules, micrometers, and sealed boxes of Nu-Kote carbon paper we're saving for the right buyers, collectors, and/or museums. We made a living honestly—without driving around the countryside, searching out newspaper-cluttered driveways, then relieving people of their jammed manuals.

Our hobby ended abruptly though, all because of, oddly enough, the president. I don't know why this particular man came out post-dusk, or why he didn't wear a bullet-proof vest, being in the business he was in. He showed up to ask if we could donate to the upcoming election. Who did that anymore, house to house? I wondered. Did we miss something on the news? Did they take away the president's website, too? The man held a clipboard that didn't work for a shield. He kept a donation pad to fill out, maybe for taxes, I don't know.

Looking back, I bet he had a scam of his own. I bet he didn't really collect donations for the president.

The guy was short—not over five feet tall—so his crotch stood right about where an average-sized man's kneecap might hover. I don't care what political party a man's affiliated with, he doesn't deserve getting shot in the nuts, even though it might keep him from siring children who'll vote in a reckless manner.

This guy didn't drag a leg backwards, like the others. No, he went straight to the sheriff's department, and the next thing you know I had to explain my NO TRESPASSING signs, plus how I thought the guy's clipboard was one of those martial arts throwing star weapons. I'd come up with these excuses before we even started. I wanted to cover all bases, you know.

Anyway, after we got found not guilty—anyone in South Carolina has a right to shoot a stranger, it seems, NO TRESPASSING signs or not—we got in the car and drove home. I guess we'd already decided to quit the game, though we never mentioned it to one another. I don't know about Nita, but I thought, What might happen if a Girl Scout shows up after dark, wanting only to sell Thin Mints or Tagalongs? We concluded that we'd either have to move to a not-ghost town or live a life of boredom. We switched to gin.

122

WHITE TRASH FISHING
Ron Rash

When the necktie around my collar feels like a noose, and
I'm weary of air-conditioning and fluorescent lights and people who
never say "He don't" or "Co-cola"; when I find myself in agreement
with my NASCAR-obsessed cousin who claims if it ain't got wheels it
ain't a sport; when Pabst Blue Ribbon tastes better than Guinness and
I want to drink it in cinderblock death-traps with names like Betty's
Lounge and The Last Chance; when I hanker for pork rinds and those
deviled eggs you barehand out of a gallon jar; when I tire of eating
animals and (yes, my dear vegetarian friends) plants that someone else
has done the messy business of killing for me; when my wife says what's
got into you and makes it clear whatever it is is no good thing; then I
begin to long for muddy water and fish with poisonous fins and faces
like nightmares, and I know there is only one thing to do: I haul a rusty
tackle box and two Zebco 404 rods and reels out of the basement and
go white trash fishing.

What I'm talking about is nothing like trout fishing on the
Beaverkill, or Henry's Fork, or in the Smokies, or the spring creeks of
Pennsylvania or any of the other meccas of the sport where men and
women with fly rods pose midstream as if on the cover of an L.L. Bean
catalog and would no more harm their catch than their dogs or children.

What I'm talking about is not largemouth bass fishing either,
especially its current manifestation as symbol of the New South: a
high-tech sport requiring sonar and radar equipment as sophisticated
as a nuclear submarine's installed on boats swift as some airplanes so
the angler can zig-zag across the monstrous reservoirs that fuel the New
South and thus compete with hundreds of other fishermen similar-
ly equipped in championships where fish are kept in a live well until
weighed, photographed, psychoanalyzed and who knows what else
before being tossed back or mounted on a wall.

What I'm talking about is killing what you catch and eating it right there on the riverbank. And I'm talking about a river, not some gin-clear stream or reservoir, because that's where white trash fishing is best done, a river where the water's the color of coffee with cream and a trout or bass would go belly up before it swam five feet. I'm talking about sitting on a riverbank littered with beer cans, bait containers, potato chip bags, used diapers, used condoms, rotting newspapers, rotting blankets and just about anything you'd care (or not care) to imagine.

It really doesn't matter what the place looks like because I'm talking about night fishing and even if the place looked like the Yellowstone River I wouldn't be able to see it anyway. The only reason I'll even be here while the sun's still up is to stake a claim to a spot and get the rods and reels rigged up and the Coleman lantern and stove set up, fueled, and primed for later.

And this is what else I bring: frying pan, corn meal, Crisco, and onions, a mess kit, a cooler filled with ice and PBR, bug spray (though it doesn't do much good), a sleeping bag, a plastic tarp in case it rains, a pistol, the bait, and, of course, what I'm wearing.

And this is what I wear: a cap that says Catfish Fishermen Do It All Night or I Don't Care How They Do It Up North and the rankest jeans and shirt I can scrounge up out of the attic or bottom drawer, because even if I don't catch a fish, the bait will leave a permanent reek on my clothes. Because what I'm talking about is that I'm after catfish, the aquatic equivalent to a possum in that they will eat anything they can grub up off the river bottom. There is no concern about "matching the hatch" or whether to use a green or a white skirt on a spinnerbait. If a catfish finds it, it'll eat it. The problem is it's moving blind down there, especially in the middle of the night, so I've got to help the fish out by giving him something he can smell. What I'm talking about is purple nightcrawlers threaded on a hook like shish kebab. What I'm talking about are doughballs textured with anything from motor oil to ketchup. I'm talking about whatever will get the job done.

When the sun finally goes down it's time to bait the rigs and cast into the dark and listen for a splash to know I didn't snag a willow. Then I sit down on the bank or a stump or maybe a lawn chair someone left, take a beer from the cooler, and wait.

It might be a while, but when I feel tugs from the dark more insistent than the current, I tighten the line and jerk for all I'm worth. I'm not talking finesse here. The object is not giving the fish "a sporting chance." What I'm talking about is setting the hook hard enough to drive the barb into the fish's brain and settle it once and for all right then. I don't "play" the catfish until it tires. I've got thirty pound test line and unless the fish wraps it around a junk car or refrigerator (and yes, there are cars and refrigerators down there along with anything else someone could throw or push into a river) it's not going to break the line, so I reel it in quick as I can and heave it onto the bank. I'm not talking about second chances when a fish flops back into the water when the hook is taken out—I'm talking rocks, tire irons, anything that can whack the fish into a limp silence.

And after I've caught enough I skin and clean the fish then put the frying pan on the stove and roll some chopped-up onions and corn meal into something that looks a lot like what I've been fishing with to make hushpuppies and then I lay the catfish in the pan. I get another beer from the cooler and when the last fish is fried I sit there and eat and sip the beer and listen to the frogs and the crickets and the river itself as it rubs against the bank. And when I finish I unroll the sleeping bag. I take out the pistol and fire off a round at the sky to keep anybody else on the river at a distance. Then I snuff the lantern and sleep so deep it's like I'm under the river, not beside it.

Come mid-morning the sun filters through the trees and I wake up. I'm cotton-mouthed and swollen with mosquito and chigger bites. I'm smelly and sweaty, my hands and clothes sticky with bait and fish slime. My head feels like somebody with a tire pump stuck the needle in my ear and didn't quit pumping until he'd doubled my hat size. But that's OK, because I will feel cleansed and somehow redeemed as I stumble up the trail to my car.

THREE DAYS AT THE OPEN
Jennifer Paddock

Day One (Sunday-Practice Day)

You start in the viewing gallery at the practice courts. You
hear him first. He has a distinctive grunt, Andrey Rublev, when he's
demolishing forehands. He's a lithe, young, blond Russian, wearing a
green Nike shirt, green headband, and green wristband. You are with
a friend, looking down from above, a view you get from television,
though across five courts, which is not a normal way to watch tennis,
with your head moving player to player, side by side, instead of following the ball.

Canadian Denis Shapovalov, another blond rising star of Russian descent, is practicing on Grandstand, the futuristic-looking, circular arena. Shapovalov is in a white shirt, trademark backwards baseball
cap, also white. His mom is in long sleeves and long pants. Working as
a tennis coach in Alabama, you understand that look. You'll do about
anything to protect yourself from the sun. She looks just like Denis—
blond, long-limbed, same height, same gait. Most of the seats are
empty, and you watch Shapovalov leap into his one-handed backhand
exquisitely, crush forehands rhythmically. It looks like he makes contact
with the ball at his pocket, rather than out in front. This cheers you up,
as you feel like the older you get, the later you hit. Watching this nine-
teen-year-old, you think of that halcyon summer when you were nine
and you beat everyone 6-0, 6-0 and timed the ball nicely in front, like
Federer. Or that's your memory.

Next we watch Jean-Julien Rojer and Horia Tecău practice
on Court 11, and the stands are full. They won the doubles last year.
Through lucky timing, you had a picture taken with Rojer. He told you
to hold the trophy, too, so it'd look like you won mixed.

Lastly, you stumble onto Daniel Nestor, a lefty, almost forty-six,
a Canadian who is a legendary doubles player. Nestor seems serene,
unaware of the few watchers. It's getting dark, and the court lights

blink on.

Day Two (Monday-First Day of the Tournament)

You watch Kyle Edmund first. His Nike shirt is half white, half blackish-blue, with a thick orange diagonal stripe. It seems bold for the quietness of Edmund, but his game is bold, with that forehand that blasts through the air.

You leave for the new fourteen-thousand seat Louis Armstrong Stadium with a retractable roof to see world No. 1 Simona Halep. But it turns out she's already lost. "Maybe the noise in the crowd," she says afterward. "The city is busy. So everything together? I'm a quiet person, so maybe I like the smaller places."

You're there for the start of the Andy Murray match. The crowd noise reverberates off the roof and through the stadium. Murray is on a comeback, recovering from hip surgery. Your seats are courtside, in the corner opposite the players' box, and in the shade. The players' box is in the sun, and you watch Andy's wife, Kim, fanning herself with her credentials. You spot his coach, Jamie Delgado, and his mother, Judy, also a tennis coach. (The night before Judy was at the same place as you for dinner—a Midtown Greek restaurant—and you felt such a thrill seeing her.) They all seem calm and don't seem to mind when Andy has his angry one-way discussions with them. Andy has become your hero. Two years ago he was No. 1 in the world and now he just wants to play. You always think that a tennis match is a perfect metaphor for life. Your birthday is coming up, September 2nd. You survived another year. You're happy to be alive. Murray is playing this match with fire and freedom, which is a pretty great formula for how to live your life.

Later that night, in Grandstand, you arrive late to a match you've been anticipating between friends and fellow Canadians Denis Shapovalov and Felix Auger-Aliassime. It's one set all, and there should be hours left, but instead Auger-Aliassime has to retire because his heart rate won't slow down. Shapovalov goes to the other side of the net, hugs his friend. They are both crying. It's a truly frightening and beautiful moment. Denis says in the on-court interview that he told

Felix, "We're going to be back here, we're going to be playing in the finals, this is just one match. We're going to have so many of these."

It's been an emotional day. You're thinking of going back to the hotel, but then you hear an announcement that Dominic Thiem is next. You've never seen him play in person. He's amazing. You think, *He could win this tournament.* Your friend notices how he spreads his fingers as he raises his arm on the serve and also on the forehand, like he's playing a scale on the piano. "He is from Austria," you say, and you imagine a view of the central square in Vienna, a city you've always wanted to visit. One of the best things about the US Open is hearing all the different languages around you—it's such a global sport. Being a tennis fan makes you feel like a citizen of the world.

Day Three (Tuesday-Second Day of the Tournament)

Extreme heat. The numbers you hear are 109 on court, feels like 118 with the humidity. As you're waiting to go inside Court 11, under an awning in the shade, to watch Americans Amanda Anisimova and Taylor Townsend, the usher says, "Enjoy this moment. It's the coolest you're going to feel all day."

She's right. It takes about five minutes to be drenched in sweat. You can't imagine how the players are doing it. At least they have ice towels. When they split sets, you leave for shady, loud Armstrong. Angelique Kerber is in a battle, but like great champions do, she finds a way to win.

You've kind of recovered from being so sweaty, and it's starting to cool down. You head to the practice courts. Federer is supposed to be there soon. The viewing gallery is packed, so you sit in the bleachers that are near the players' entrance. You have to watch through a black chain-linked fence, but it's still a nice view. You arrive about the same time twenty-year-old Greek star Stefanos Tsitsipas is coming on court. He's 6'4", sinewy, with long flowing hair, and an angular, handsome face. He moves as though he's starring in an arty movie, and the director has slowed down time for effect. Your friend whispers to you discreetly without turning her head, "He just looked at us. But I feel kind of funny because we're more than twice his age." You smile and say, "Maybe he just recognizes kindred spirits, fellow dreamers." Tsitsipas looks around a lot, though he's quiet and does what his coaches tell him. He begins hitting crosscourts, your favorite tennis drill, and is in full flow, especially when you see him separate his arms on his backhand. You think, *He's the best player I've seen. He could win this whole tournament.*

You hear the roar of a crowd that's been gathering. You see phones raised and clicking and kids with giant tennis balls and sharpies. You know he's there, but you don't see him yet. Then the great man appears, Roger Federer, strolling across Practice Court 5. Tsitsipas watches—you've read that Federer is his idol, but he doesn't give that away in his glance. Federer looks more like he's floating, in the heat haze, as he gets farther away. He walks with nothing—someone else is carrying his racquet bag to Practice Court 1. Federer is transcendent.

Then you watch him apply sunscreen—his hands touch his face like anyone doing this—and he seems human. Until his first swing. "A great liquid whip," David Foster Wallace called his forehand. And it is *the* Federer forehand with that slingshot looseness. *He is Federer*, you think. *He could easily win this whole thing.* But then your eyes go back to Tsitsipas. You can't really tear them away. But you do. You think of Federer as the past/present, Tsitsipas as the present/future. Federer is 37 and Tsitsipas is 20, though maybe on the court, you all feel like kids. You think, *Time is not real. Time is an illusion.* You and your friend watch for an hour until Tsitsipas's practice ends and he sits on the bench resting, and you imagine, sealing this moment in his memory.

The sun is beginning to set. You rest on the benches between the Media Center and Courts 5, 6 & 7, which have matches on, but are so crowded that you can't see the players. You don't really care. You've just witnessed the most amazing visual and on the hottest day you remember at the Open.

Tsitsipas will lose the next day. So will Murray. Shapovalov will lose in the third round. Federer will lose in the fourth.

But these are just matches. We're all going to be back here. We're going to have so many of these.

MY BREAK
FROM *WALKING IN THE LIGHT*
Theodore Pitsios

Ordinary people seem to think a man has to have luck on his side to make it big in life. That's the ordinary people. I believe a man has to have the balls to go looking for his luck instead of sitting, waiting for luck to find him and pull him by the hand. And most important, a man has to have enough sense to recognize when he's getting a lucky break and jump on it.

I shifted on the mattress, trying to get away from a broken spring, and once again told myself, *It was a damn lucky break I got, no matter how bleak things seem to be right now.* I adjusted my head on the pillow and resumed staring at the ceiling. I had taken a long time to fall asleep last night, my mind reliving everything that happened the last three days on the road from Hoboken to Miami. I should have been dead tired, but instead the first light of day found me wide awake, staring at the ceiling, creating imaginary shapes out of the water stains. *That dark one, the one over the door, looks like a loaded mule. This long one right over me looks like three naked women line dancing. And the rust-colored one near the window, that could be my old ship, the Aegean Sea.*

It could be the new environment—I was used to the ship's gentle rolling and the rhythmic sound of the sea splashing against the sides—or it could be that I was too excited. After all, this was not going to be an ordinary day. This Friday, the first day of October of 1965, I would be starting my first job in America, my first step toward making it big in life.

I stretched again, then continued studying the ceiling stains. They were floodlit by early sun rays filtering through the newspaper taped over the window. *That big brown one definitely looks like my old ship.* Only seventy-two hours had passed since I'd left her, but already it seemed like something that had happened a long time ago. Right now the old rust bucket should be somewhere in the Atlantic, pounding the waves on her way to Aruba. The two deckhands filling in for me would

130

probably be having a snack in the crew's lounge, griping about what crumbs they were getting paid for overtime. And with their engine room watch over, Anastasis and Liapouras would be there too, playing backgammon for one cigarette a game.

Liapouras, who had lived a few months in Boston and knew everything about everything, would be repeating in his squeaky voice for the umpteenth time, "I knew Kostas Karaoglou would jump ship as soon as we got to America. He didn't fool me, not for one minute, he didn't." A typical ship's crew, all of them. Ordinary people with small dreams and short horizons, happy in their own little world, boasting of their petty triumphs, trying to outwit and out-insult each other, completely oblivious when a life-changing break hit them right the face.

I spotted my lucky break the day I signed on the *Aegean Sea* and the steward put me in the same cabin with Telemahos. It took just a few minutes talking with him to sense that he and I thought the same way. He had worked in Savannah, in America, for over a year, he told me, until a bastard squealed to immigration and they shipped him back to Greece. He was going to try it again, he said, and after he beat the daylights out of that squealer shit-pot in Savannah, he would go to work in Miami.

"There is a man in Miami who owns a fancy restaurant and a luxury apartment rental business. His family owes my family big favors, and he told my folks he'll give me a job there anytime I want," Telemahos told me.

I convinced him that for an undertaking like this, an extra pair of eyes would be an advantage, so we made the ship-jumping plans together.

The light was coming in through the window stronger now, and I gave the room another look. Until I was legal, this would be my home. If I got rid of some of the junk, it would be as big as the biggest room in my mother's house. I could put a closet in the far corner and a table with a chair by the window, to sit and look out. *The hard part is almost over. All I have to do now is lie low and stay out of trouble.*

I knew the good life would be here soon. Not bad for a start— better than most people, with their small dreams, their petty grievances, and their short, sad horizons.

THE WALKER
Karen Spears Zacharias

We met on a narrow pathway in Prestwick between two stone houses. I was looking for a fish and chips spot about five miles up the road from the Tam O'Shanter where Robert Burns is said to have downed more than a few pints. Initially, I'd stopped to ask if she knew the way to the beach biking route. A merchant in Ayr said there was a promenade where a person could ride a bike between Ayr and Prestwick. He failed to mention all the detours a person would have to take along the way.

My first detour was the pier in town. I hadn't accounted for the River Ayr which fed into the Firth of Clyde, necessitating that I ride over the bridge before trying to find the route. I'd biked a half-hour-or-so before that ride was cut short by a golf course. I didn't have a clue where I was, but I was greeted by warning signs: "Bikers Walk. No Biking Allowed." I was still astride my bike when I entered the narrow pathway. My companion, Ellen, was walking her bike and calling out to me to pay attention to the signs I was ignoring. I hopped off the bike after the pathway took a turn to the left and I nearly ran smack dab into The Walker.

Apologizing for my lack of consideration, I asked if she happened to know where the fish place was. She turned up her nose.

"It's no' good," she said.

"Really?" I said, surprised. The place had been recommended by an administrator at the campus where I was studying. He was enthusiastic about it. Given the only fish I'd had since arriving in Scotland was some tasteless grocery store salmon and some mass-produced fast-food yuk, I was disappointed by her reaction.

"Aye, mabbie it's different no'. Ah haven't eaten thare since before th' pandemic." The Walker went on to explain that back when she was growing up in the town, it was the fish place to go to. "Ah dinnae wanna tae pat ye aff it." She offered directions and made sure to warn that there were two fish places near each other. "Fin' th' one closest a th' church."

"Thank you," I said. "We will do that."

"Ar' ye from Canada or America?" she asked.

"America," Ellen replied.

"You ever been?" I asked.

"No," The Walker replied. "Ah grew up he'e. Mah faither wis Scot. My mum was from Burma."

Never ask a Scot a question without expecting a story in return. We spent the next half-hour listening as the sun set over the Firth and as The Walker shared her family's history.

"My po' mum. Kin ye imagine? Mah faither stuck her oot 'ere with four wee ones. He wis a'ways gawn, workin'. She ne'er wanted tae be 'ere. She missed Burma."

I didn't tell The Walker but I could imagine. There was a time when my husband took me to a small rural Oregon community to live. It was so far back in the woods they piped in sunshine, as the saying goes. We had four children, ages five and under. I had never lived in such a rural place. Nor had I ever lived in a place where it snowed … for months on end. Our rental was located half a block from the school where Tim was teaching. The only heat in the house was a wood stove. I didn't know how to make a wood stove fire, or apparently to keep one going.

Tim would make a fire in the mornings before he left for work. He would return at lunch to stoke the fire or start it again if it had died out. He'd do the same after school and before coaching football or basketball. And again when he came home for the night. It was always cold in that house. Temperatures dropped down to 40 below for two weeks during our first year there. I couldn't figure out why the car wouldn't start. I was trapped in the house with four preschoolers, three of them in diapers. I thought I was going to lose my mind. Instead, I took up sewing as a last resort. And if you understood how much I hate sewing, you'd appreciate the irony of that pursuit. I did end up in therapy for three of the four years we lived there. And I joined a writer's group at the library and found my other true love.

I nodded in empathy as The Walker continued her story about her poor mother. They had met in Burma when her father was stationed there during the war. He swept her off her feet in one of those whirlwind wartime romances. The kind that rarely pan out. She had no idea when she married him it would mean moving away from her parents, from her homeland. Who ponders such things when caught up in the want of another?

"Mah mither wis preg'ant wi' me whin it was time tae move 'ere. Mah sisters were born in Burma. But mah mither git tae feeling poorly and couldn't travel so Ah wis born in Burma, tae. We moved tae Glasgow, 'n' that wasn't so bad. Ah had an aunt in Glasgow. But whin mah faither moved mah mither 'ere, it was tac much fur her."

"Did your mother take her own life?" I asked.

"Aye. She tried. One Christmas, she teuk a blade 'n' cut her wrists. Mah dad pat her in a head hospital. Mah granny come bade wi' us until Mum was better. It was an awfly bad time."

The minute the question was out of my mouth, I was mortified that I had asked it. I understood why I had asked it. There was something in the way The Walker spoke of her mother. She had such deep empathy for the woman her mother had been. She understood at her age something of the isolation her young mother had experienced.

I had written a novel about a young mother in the throes of post-partum psychosis (*Mother of Rain*), which led me to a lode of articles about the mental health struggles of mothers of young children. The isolation of being a stay-at-home mother can exacerbate depression for women. And children who grow up with mothers coping with depression often struggle with depression as well. Research suggests that suicide is the leading cause of maternal death in the U.S. (Mostafavi, 2020). Every area of a woman's life is affected with the onset of children, from the condition of her body to the health of her mind, to the setbacks in career pursuits. I once heard a radio show in which the educator being interviewed said the biggest hindrances to a woman's professional life are marriage, motherhood, and money. I could see The Walker wrestling with the sacrifices her mother had made on behalf of all her daughters. Daughters are more forgiving of the failures of their mothers once they become mothers.

As she spoke, The Walker's cell phone would prompt her to get moving again, ordering her around like a pocket nanny. The Walker explained that her son was getting married, and she was trying to get in shape for the wedding, so she walks from Ayr to Prestwick and back every day. Her phone boss wanted her to get a move on.

"Ah've put on twenty stones because of COVID," she said. "Ah'm tae short for the weight. Ah'm only 5'4"."

Ellen and I assured her she looked lovely and strong.

"Ah hav' royal blood in me," she said, and I had no reason to doubt her. As far as I'm concerned, every woman over sixty is a queen. Or deserves to be treated like one.

We bade goodbye to a new friend and made our way into town along the promenade as she directed. It took us a good half-hour to find the fish place, even with her specific directions that it was across the street from the church. Scotland is like Georgia in that there is a church on every corner. We kept backtracking between the first three we happened upon. Turns out the fish place was between the third and fourth steeple.

The fried fish was better than promised and worth the circuitous ride it took to get us there. Ellen and I sat on the stone wall of the fourth church and shared a box dinner of breaded fish fillets and watched the dogs parade past, pulling at their leashes, hoping we'd drop a chip.

Not a chance. We needed the fuel for the ride back.

THE BOYS
Patricia Foster

Let's say it begins in Beijing with the boys, perhaps a little boy who toddles from his mother to a blade of grass, a bright greenish twig secretly calling to him, pulling him toward its demanding hum. He bends over in his red apron-like garment, its sturdy straps tied around his waist and thighs, his naked buttocks thrust out into the air. Or maybe it begins with a boy in diapers, peeking from behind a bamboo curtain while we Americans eat soft, moist tofu in an upstairs restaurant, our chopsticks clicking. "Chinese tofu!" we squeal, the taste so succulent, so rich, we keep turning the lazy-Susan, round and round, reaching for more. Or perhaps it begins with the startled face of a bristly headed boy poked by my umbrella as I am pushed and shoved by curious crowds through the last ornate gate of the Forbidden City. Our bodies are packed so close I wonder how the adults free an arm to touch the thick red walls, their fingers caressing that rough painted surface for happiness, good fortune, and the miracle of love while the boy gazes steadily at me, his round face as smooth as polished stone. He looks more startled than hurt, but that face, it's such a sweet boy's face, I keep saying, "I'm sorry, I'm so sorry" long after he's turned away.

Much later I'll realize it begins with Kim and Mieka, two boys who run dutifully towards me in the park after the Chinese man, Harry, their English language coach, calls out, "A teacher. Come meet the teacher," as if he's discovered a prize. And there I am trapped in my duties, caught in a profession I want to leave behind as I wander through Hepingli Park on this bright July morning. There are times when I long to be just a citizen, irrelevant to the world, bemused or indifferent, self-absorbed and myopic, useless to anyone, merely a traveler, scavenging for scraps of delight that mean nothing to anyone else. But now I have been found. A teacher. I know the part.

Kim, the taller boy, reaches out to shake my hand, his own hand so soft it makes me blush. Then Mieka, his mouth tucked sideways to repress a grin. He knows this is all a show for the English coach, Harry. What does Mieka care? Left to his own desires, he'd probably give me a high five and sprint off to swimming or badminton or talking loud to his friends. But now, like me, he's caught. He turns that round puckish face towards me, his two front teeth overlapping, his forehead so narrow he is all dark eyes and black brows. His hair, barely a bristle of dark fuzz, reveals an emerging cowlick. I smile. For him I will be a teacher. While he shifts from foot to foot, Kim stands attentively, staring at me with dark, solemn eyes behind wire-rimmed glasses. His eyes say, "I'm here. I'm listening. I'm a boy who is going places."

"*Nice to meet you,*" Kim says precisely, in a voice as soft as his hand. "*How are you?*" comes out stronger, more assured. I imagine he will be a businessman someday, traveling the world, calling from a distant shore, surprised at how easily his words shift–like a warm, sweet breath–from Mandarin to English and back to Mandarin.

"*Nice,*" Mieka says, tossing out the one word he knows, mimicking his friend. He too holds out his hand even as the coach says emphatically "*to meet you!*"

Let's say it begins with two handshakes and becomes the inevitable conversation of *How old? How much you like? What you do here? How long you stay? Where you live?*

"No, no," Harry intones. "Never ask age."

Kim frowns at the mistake, but quickly recovers. "Where from?"

Ahhh, near Chicago. A smile.

It begins when Harry, the English coach, saw me sitting alone in the park at 8:30 on a Sunday morning in July. As he walked past, he turned and smiled at me, then idled near the pond, glancing my way. I sat on a stone bench on a tiled square beneath the shade of poplar trees and watched an old man across from me fiddle with something I couldn't quite comprehend. At first, I thought he was opening a tube, like a Pringles tube of potato chips, perhaps his breakfast, but instead of breakfast, it became a long, flat brush he attached to a stick. Still, I didn't understand. The old man, dressed in a loose white t-shirt and baggy pants with a faded blue hat squashed flat on his head, glanced slyly at me–the interloper–then went back to his work. I watched as he limped to the pond and dipped the brush into the still water. Then, to my surprise, he limped back and began to paint: long, rhythmic sweeps on the gray tiled ground, a calligraphy of brushed water.

"Oh," I murmured. "Beautiful."

It was then that Harry appeared by my side. "Can you tell me what he is writing?" I asked after Harry had introduced himself.

Harry stepped closer to the man, gazing at the winged characters. "He is writing poetry," he said. "Here, look, he is writing about faraway places." He stared at me. "You see? About heaven and earth. You understand heaven and earth?"

I nodded, uncertain if I did.

"He is saying we must get as far away as we can."

Though I'm not sure I understand, I imagine he means that our spiritual selves must try to grasp heaven, must try to hold both heaven and earth in our bodies, finding a heaven both within and beyond this earth. *As far away as we can.* And though I know he means this philosophically, I can't help thinking of the literal, of how much time I've spent trying to get as far away as I can, as if faraway places might save me, might allow me to find a heaven within by exploring the world without. But it's more than that. I have expected the world to save me from silence, to infuse me with speech. Often as a child I was too frightened to speak. Each night I lay in bed, a ghost-child beside my sister, the one who talked so much her 5th grade teacher kept her in for an entire year of recess. She talked and she read. She read at the dinner table, talked in church, read in the middle of softball games and talked all through the movies we paid eight dollars to see. She told my parents everything she did as if she had no censors, no shame, had nothing to hide, but how could that be? I was a child full of cautions, ellipses, living in an insular world, always watching. I watched the physical irritation of my father, how his eyes jerked and his mouth narrowed at the slightest interruption. I watched that same face relax with sudden, irrepressible joy, his jaw softened, all his teeth showing. I watched my sister sneeze and forget to catch the sneeze with a Kleenex, and then forget that sneezes mattered, that the sneeze *went* somewhere. I watched the rain puddle the yard, making huge, pond-sized puddles where frogs, tiny as walnuts, leapt and splashed. I watched and in the moment of watching, I was happy. Only later, when the spell was broken, did I perceive how quiet I had been, and in such moments, I believed it was the silence that made me invisible, unreachable, a girl hiding behind the door. From this premise came a private admonition: I must become a grand and fanciful creature, a creature who wanted to talk. Surely a faraway place would be my rescue, my tutor. A faraway place would become my experience, something to talk about, to take home as my prize. And yet ironically, each new place—London in my twenties, Dublin in my thirties, Florence in my fifties—pulled me back into silence, into my watchful, watching self.

Perhaps that's why I notice the boys in Beijing, so mischievous, so surprising. Yesterday I watched three little boys following their parents into the Yonghegong Lama Temple. The oldest boy knelt, bowing at one of the altars, his hands holding his incense sticks upright as he bent low, his forehead almost touching the ground. He looked reverent, devout. I watched as he rose in one fluid motion and very carefully placed his incense stick on the altar. And then to my surprise, he turned to his brothers, two fingers holding his nose, his grin barely stifled.

I laughed.

The boys. I see them everywhere. With backpacks and Mickey Mouse t-shirts. With orange flip-flops and tennis shoes. With #10 written on the brim of their caps. With fishing rods and badminton rackets. With cell phones and bicycles. They sneak into my consciousness and take me away from myself, and for a moment I forget to worry. I am watching.

"Goodbye. Nice to talk," Kim says when I tell them I must leave the park for a meeting.

"I am so glad to have met you," I say. "I am so glad to have come to your country, to your city, Beijing."

Harry smiles a gleeful smile. Then he prods Mieka.

"Good," Mieka says, his eyebrows raised as if he hopes this is right. He smiles at me and then he takes a small step forward so that he is slightly in front of Kim. "Good," he says again, more assertive this time.

And I nod, repeating his word—*Good!*—but what I'm seeing are the sensuous curves and arches of the poet's characters, their bones thickening into symbols of heaven and earth, then fading, becoming fragments, as fleeting as rain evaporating into clouds. As I walk away, I carry them inside even as they vanish in the mid-day sun.

LEAVING VERMONT
From *LUMPERS, LONGNECKS, AND ONE-EYED JACKS*
Joe Formichella

Victor danced on the cold flagstones that wound down from the front porch of the old farmhouse. He hopped from one bare foot to the other, rubbing the bottom of each elevated foot against the opposite shin for some warmth before shifting his bulky weight again. Only the first week of October, mornings were already cold in Vermont, overnight temperatures dipping into the thirties, threatening freezing. Zimmer watched Victor hop, rub, hop, knowing what was coming.

"You sure you got to go?"

Victor kept asking him the same question. That's what happened to him in the winter, as if the effort to stay warm became such a preoccupation that everything else was narrowed down to singular, obsessive lines of inquiry or expression or activity. This was just the first indication, but Zimmer knew what was coming. He'd already spent a couple of winters with Victor, and Jessie, their kids. The faint grey puffs of condensed air that Victor grunted out from all the exertion were a kind of sign that Zimmer could read well enough.

"You sure you got to go?"

"I can't stay, but thanks for asking."

Victor had to think about that, hopping, rubbing. He looked like a circus bear, performing. He was big enough, certainly, six-two, two-fifty, or about. And he was hairy enough, his full head of dark tangles sticking out in various directions. His beard was both untrimmed, and unruly, reaching from just under his eye sockets all the way down his neck so that it kind of blended into his chest hair. And Zimmer knew that he was just as hairy, and completely naked beneath the faded red terry-cloth bathrobe.

Victor knew no shame. It was a trait that both fascinated and scared Zimmer. The fascination was starting to swallow him up. He couldn't imagine another idle winter in Vermont. Two had been too much, already.

"You sure you got to go?"

"Yeah, I got to."

"You don't even have any heat in that thing," Victor reminded him, motioning with his chin in the general direction of Zimmer's car, the light blue VW Beetle.

"That's one reason to go now," Zimmer said, surveying the morning sky. It looked like rain, or worse. "Before we have any of those nights where the battery freezes."

"And you need new tires. You need a new starter. Fuck, Z, you'll never make it."

"Shut up, Victor."

"All right, all right. Why Florida? Why... What's that place called?"

"Panama City Beach."

"Sounds like it has an identity problem."

"I spent a weekend there, a few years ago. Seemed like a nice place."

"What, you gonna start surfing or something?"

"I don't know."

"All right," Victor said, bending and reaching behind the porch steps for a mayonnaise jar and holding it out to Zimmer. "If you say you got to, I guess you got to."

Zimmer took the jar, saw mostly hundred dollar bills stuffed into it. "What's this?"

"Christmas bonus."

"Victor, this is too much. You're crazy."

"Forget it," he said, grinning through his beard. "Take it, in case you break down. Or if you find any good dope down there, send it our way. And you know you can come back, if you get bored."

"Bored?"

After two and half years with Victor, being bored was probably what Zimmer needed most. At the very least, he yearned for the peacefulness and isolation that always came with driving. He needed the peacefulness of solitude, the isolation of the open road, so that he'd only have himself and his own voices to answer to.

He knew one thing, at least. He had to leave Vermont. He had to leave Athens, anyway, leave Victor, and Jessie, and the kids. He absolutely knew that. He could feel it. And he could hear it, driving. To the constant whine of the VW's tires he would answer, "Got to go. Got to."

By the time he was nearing the Vermont border, south of Brattleboro, cruising opposite all the chartered tourist buses on their annual leaf pilgrimages, he'd already told himself a couple of thousand times, "You've got to go, got to."

Zimmer talked to himself a lot. He's spent most of his near thirty years alone, or trying to become alone, and it's an easy habit he's developed, letting thoughts out loud. He talked to himself all through New England—Massachusetts, Connecticut. Talked a little louder, and not always to himself, as he made his way through White Plains, Mount Vernon, to the tip of Manhattan where he escaped across the GWB—the "busiest bridge in the world"—for Fort Lee, New Jersey.

Before he knew it, he was in Paterson, remembering a Dylan song, *Hurricane*, singing, "Why'd you bring him in here for, he ain't the guy..." settling into a zone.

He didn't want to feel any urgency, didn't want to hurry. He welcomed the idleness of driving, "The chance to become bored," cruising westward, slicing into Pennsylvania. He wasn't even working from a map, by design. Victor had pulled a Rand McNally out of a kitchen drawer and tried to draw a route for Zimmer to take, down the coast, zig-zagging the larger cities.

"You can fly on the Jersey Turnpike," he said. "Between toll booths. There's a beltway around Baltimore, and Washington. I'm not sure about Atlanta."

"Atlanta?"

"Got to go through Atlanta."

No, he didn't. He looked at the map long enough to find Panama City and trace the big green veins of interstate—he didn't want to have anything to do with toll booths, actually—back to Vermont, in straight lines and right angles, a simple, direct approach. He was headed for Ohio.

"That's crazy."

"He said."

"You'll add hours to your trip."

"Doesn't matter."

Truth was, he wanted to steer clear of New York, which was easy enough. There were too many memories there, unfinished memories, and he was afraid he'd be tempted to go back and try to work them out. He neither wanted to do that, nor did he want to drag any of them along, south. He wanted new. He wanted to start over completely. If he learned nothing else from the experience in Vermont, he learned you couldn't fix some things, unlike car repair, say. Once gone wrong, there was very little chance to recover fully. There would always be vestigial questions. While there might be answers, he'd probably never have *The* answer. And sometimes, the only answer left was nothing. Forget it. Leave.

LEFT BEHIND
Frank Turner Hollon

Edward Tuttle sat perfectly still in the chair on the wooden porch behind his trailer. It was a warm morning, and the sixty-three-year-old wore a light blue terrycloth robe and brown bedroom slippers. He leaned forward slightly in the chair with his right arm cocked, holding a hammer, the metal resting lightly against his unshaven cheek. The small black-and-white cat peered from her place beside the wheel of the trailer. A bowl of cat food waited at the old man's feet.

Three months earlier Deloris Tuttle had packed her shit and left. For thirty-three years she had awakened every morning in Edward's bed, but when the time came to make the decision to leave, she was unnaturally swift. In less than one hour she was completely gone—clothes, kitchen utensils, photographs, and twelve of her thirteen cats—in the car, out the driveway, gone away. As he watched his wife gather her possessions, Edward felt as though he were watching a television show. At the end he actually said, "Don't let the door hit you in the ass on the way out." He said it too late. Deloris Tuttle was already gone.

She'd left before, but this time was different. This time she took the cats. Through the years, no matter where they moved, or what financial crisis they faced, there was one constant. The cats. They were always there, underfoot, swarming across the kitchen floor. A choking cloud of cat urine hovered around their home. And hair. Cat hair. Everywhere. Edward could rub his hand across the couch and fill his fingers full.

A cat door was installed. The beasts came and went as they pleased, their pink noses high in the air, with the never-ending ungodly whining. For years Edward tried to round up the females and have them fixed in a futile effort to control the sheer numbers. It couldn't be done. New cats would appear, breed, and then disappear. One time, many years earlier, when Deloris had left him on Christmas Eve, Edward had loaded the cats in the trunk of the car and dropped them two miles away at Stilton's barn. The next morning, Christmas Day, one by one the cats returned, and later that night, so did Deloris. This time was different though. This time she took her cats away with her. Except for one: black and white, skinny, about half grown, somehow left behind.

On the first day Edward chased the frightened creature across the yard with his shovel, but the cat managed to escape. Each night the cat would sit alone on the back porch completely quiet, waiting for food. Edward watched her curiously through the window of the back door. It was a standoff. Some evenings he would sit outside and call the little cat to him. She would stand away, coy, stepping forward and then back again, Edward's fingers allowed to brush the fur lightly before the cat would circle away, lie down, and flick her white-tipped tail.

The phone never rang. Edward would pick it up from time to time and make sure it still had a dial tone. The days passed, and Edward Tuttle imagined his wife, head held high, fixing her hair in another man's mirror. He pretended to enjoy his freedom from the constant complaining, the roar of the vacuum, the stink of cats. She had taken every hairbrush, every bottle of shampoo. At night, lying alone in bed, Edward had to struggle against the feeling that Deloris was in the next room and would come to bed soon, like always. Anger and loneliness combined to form a new, completely separate, emotion.

On one certain day, without giving it much thought, Edward threw a chicken bone out the back door to the starving cat. He watched the cat crunch the bone, gnawing the marrow and gristle, not leaving a single morsel behind, nothing. After that, sometimes he would toss out a biscuit or a handful of Cheetos.

In the back of the refrigerator Edward found an old mayonnaise jar half-full of leftover brown gravy. He unscrewed the top, knelt down at the door, and rolled the open jar across the wooden back porch towards the hungry little cat. The cat was cautious, watching the jar and Edward at the same time, until it came to a stop a few feet away and the smell of the jellied gravy was too much temptation. She sniffed the opening, hesitated, and then shoved her muzzle into the jar, ears folded tightly back, lapping at the gravy. Eventually the cat's entire head was inside, tongue stretching for the farthest taste, until the glass was licked clean. And then the trouble began. The cat's head was trapped. It had gone inside easily enough, seeking the sweet taste of brown gravy, but now it wouldn't come out. Edward watched from the door. The cat panicked and then stopped, dead still. She could see Edward through the glass jar step forward onto the porch. The cat swung her head wildly, spinning backwards, with the jar crashing against a cement cinder block on the edge of the porch. The glass exploded leaving a jagged collar around her neck as she darted away to the safety of the wheel of the trailer. The sharp edges of the glass cut the skin under her chin and behind the ears. Edward stood in his pajamas, cigarette hanging between his fingers, his arms limp. He tried to figure out how he felt about what he'd just seen.

When the coast was clear, the pitiful cat eventually came back to the porch. Edward stood at the back door, and they stared at each other in total silence. Blood trickled from the cuts and scratches around the cat's neck, fresh red and matted, but she sat anyway, and waited for something. Edward Tuttle smoked his cigarette and wondered how he ever ended up in such a place staring at a goddamned cat with a jagged glass collar. He listened for the sound of a car coming up the dirt driveway, but there was nothing. No one was coming.

The next morning, early, Edward Tuttle positioned his chair in the middle of the porch. At his feet he placed a fresh bowl of cat food, and in his hand he held a hammer. It was a warm morning. He knew what a hammer could do. Edward concentrated on remaining still, feet wide apart on either side of the bowl, hammer raised at exactly the right angle. The cat watched from her spot by the tire, smelling the food on the porch, seeing the old man in his light blue terrycloth robe and brown slippers, sitting without motion in a chair. She stepped forward, stretching, with an ache in her empty belly and a burning sensation under her chin. Closer she came, and closer, smelling the fishy cat food, watching the man, until hunger overcame fear and the cat found herself face down crunching big mouthfuls. Edward steadied himself, drew his aim in his mind, and swung the hammer downward with the necessary force, eyes square on the target. It was the first thing he felt good about since the day that bitch walked out the door. Edward stood, flung the hammer in the yard, and walked inside the trailer.

SNAKEBIT
Dayne Sherman

The best dog I ever owned died two weeks back. His name was Earl. I named him after my grandpa, Earl Ned Thompson.

Grandpa liked to hunt squirrel in the morning and fox at night. After he was put in the nursing home for that old–timer's disease, he still hunted his dogs. He'd call one of his boys to come get him. Or he'd break out of the place and head to the woods on his own, hitch a ride. His body was mostly strong, but his mind had left him. They found him drowned in a gully beside the Tangilena River, drowned in a foot of water. Eighty years old and died hunting.

Earl was one of them rare breed of dogs, not one of them fuzzy biscuit eaters that lays up in the flabby lap of a subdivision woman. He was a registered Treeing Feist. And he hated squirrel like a hog hates a barbecued pork chop.

He didn't die of natural causes. His sweet little life was cut short by means of Vienna sausages floating around in a pan of anti-freeze. That's why I'm in the jailhouse now. It ain't right for a man to kill your favorite dog. You might have to go through ten or twelve head of puppies to get a squirrel dog, till you get a sure enough squirrel dog. It might take a hundred dogs before you get one like Earl. He'd treed as high as twenty-seven squirrel in one November morning. Christ, he was a squirrel dog.

I'd set up in my recliner and watch TV with him setting on my belly. His little head resting on my chest like my own kid, if I had me a kid. Like my very own son. He'd snore like a fat man. Good Lord knows hisself what a miracle a squirrel dog is when he comes into the world. Then some rotten sumbitch just takes it away from you as quick as chopping the head off a Christmas hen.

I'll tell you one thing, you'd better never mess with a feller's dog in Baxter Parish, Louisiana. See, I'd warned Olland Wicker. He wasn't from Tangilena. He came here from Metairie, a rat's nest extension of the City of New Orleans. He was a retired state worker, a fat cat run off for stealing, people say. A real smart-ass. A royal S.O.B. He bought hisself my neighbor's dairy farm at a tax sale, the Mullins place. He prowled around the gravel roads in a big dually truck all decked out. Thought he owned the road and the dirt below it. He pulled up in my gravel drive when I was cleaning a mess of catfish underneath my lean-to carport. I'd caught them on a trotline in Lake Tickfaw.

"Your little bitty dog is pissing on my wife's roses," he says, dressed in a black cowboy hat and western shirt like he was a cattleman or a bank robber. He was too stupid to know Earl was a full-blooded Treeing Feist.

I kept pulling on the yellow-brown skin of a tabby cat with the pliers. Never bothered to look up at him. I was thinking about his old lady shrieking on Friday and Saturday evenings when Wicker gets heavy on the vodka. How he beats his wife with a piece of garden hose, and she runs off into the woods to hide from him. How she never calls the law 'cause he'll beat the hell out of her again even worse. That woman's frail as a grasshopper with rheumatoid arthritis. Poor woman.

"My little dog can't drink enough water to hurt them flowers," I say, as the skin pulled free from the fishtail. I dropped the skin and fish head into the plastic five-gallon gutbucket.

That slapped him in the face. He bristled. I was looking straight at him with a thin fillet knife in my right hand that I'd picked up off the plywood table beside my skinning hook. He walked back to his truck. He says, "I got something for him."

"Wicker, you screw around with my little dog, and I might just have a little something for you."

He spun out of my yard and onto the blacktop highway. Directly, his wife went to hollering, the sound of breaking glass. He was whipping her skinny butt again.

I inherited this place, four acres and a closed-in dogtrot house, several years back when Aunt Betty died. She was a spinster, and I was her favorite forty-year-old bachelor nephew that used to look after her. I got the place in her will. Not much but it'll do me as long as I can keep the starved-blind termites away.

Earl was bad to dig out of the net-wire fence in the backyard. I went around and put bricks and chunks of concrete in Earl's dug-out spots. Didn't do no good, 'cause I had to go to work at the feed mill, and when I got home he was laying up on the front porch cool as Willie Nelson. He had to cat around. He had to ramble, actin' like a big dog in a small dog's body.

The next day he come up missing. I found him out under the back porch. Stiff as a dried raccoon pecker. Earl was swolled up, tongue curled and hanging out the side of his little black jaw. Took him to the vet for an autopsy. Wrapped him in a blanket, the one he slept on, and I brung him to old Dr. Scarborough. Doc says right off he was likely poisoned.

I missed a whole day of work, what with going to the vet and burying him. I dug his grave. He weren't nothing but a tiny thing 'cause he ain't weighed but eighteen pounds, though the stiffening of his legs made the hole have to be bigger. Then I set down and drunk a half a fifth of Early Times and listened to my Merle Haggard albums, all six of them. Worked up a bona fide funk. So, I went over to Wicker's house about one o'clock in the morning just to take a look around. All they got is cats. It wasn't like they had any warning. I slipped through the darkness, never turning on my green army flashlight, a revolver in my waistband. Found some sausages mixed in a pan of antifreeze by his pump shed, nearby some rose bushes. That's all the evidence I needed.

Wicker's mailbox was just south of mine, right down by a giant sycamore tree. The mailbox was fresh-painted, a black and white wooden thing his wife must of bought at a craft show. Made to look like a dairy cow with pink rubber tits hanging and a rope tail, fake plastic horns out front. His wife worked days at the hospital in Ruthberry. Wicker checked the mail every day hisself, and I'd seen him walk out in a pair of long-assed short britches to the box a hundred times.

I wandered down to my grape vines. I wasn't looking for no grapes. Aunt Betty had a yard full of fig trees, pears, persimmons, and a low-hung grape arbor fifty feet long. There was enough grapes rotting on the ground to make birds drunk, to make the place smell like a wino's living room, to make water moccasins rustle the leaves on the ground whenever you pass by. Some old people say that cottonmouths get fat on grapes. That ain't right. They get fat as a tick off the birds and mice that eat the grapes.

At the arbor, I was looking for one serpent in particular, Old

Stumpy. I never killed him. I'm a peaceful man. I could have shot his sorry ass a thousand times. But I figure creatures are here for a reason. God put him here for a purpose. I let him be for years. He was about four-foot long, dark as Delta dirt, big around in the middle as my wrist, and his tail come right to a flat stop in a few inches. He was a stump-tail water moccasin. Mean bastard. It took me two days slipping down to the arbor before and after work to catch him. Put a stick on his neck. Like to got struck. Stuffed him down in a big croker sack to avoid a fang. Tied it up with twine.

I drove the fertilizer truck for Mount Olive Feed Mill, LLC. And this gave me some freedom. I drove a mile away from the house over on Line Creek Road where they ain't nobody that lives there no more, only teenagers trying to get tail at night, a few deer hunters, and a lot of dopeheads cooking crystal meth. I parked the truck. Took the sack out and eased through the woods down a fire ditch cut in be-tween the pines. Twenty minutes. I watched from a blackberry thicket when Lenny dropped off the mail in Wicker's box. That was that. One o'clock accuracy. You could set your watch by Lenny Ford's mail route.

I went up to that milk cow-looking box and opened the lid. Slipped in the croker sack with Old Stumpy atop some loose mail, a circular from Wal-Mart. Untied the hay string and slung the little gate closed. Shut the wooden gate hard. Slapped the box a couple of times to give Old Stumpy cause to stew. Left out through the woods in a hurry.

I weren't there myself, but I could see Old Stumpy in my head. Mad bastard with a mouth white as snow, a mouth that could take in a rat as big as a baby possum. Angry bastard setting there waiting in the dark till Wicker slipped in his long hairy right arm, a cigarette burning in his teeth. The same arm that unlidded them Vienna sausages and mixed the antifreeze. A long arm that beat his wife.

***

They say Wicker's hand swolled up the size of a basketball. Big Cajun Ambulance Service come got him. Old Stumpy gave him brain damage of a high degree. Shut his windpipe tight as a preacher's wallet. Couldn't get no wind to his old brain. Caused a stroke, they say. He's in the nursing home in Liberty City now. All he says is "shoo-boobly-boo, shoo-boobly-boo," over and over again while he rocks back and forth in a chair. The man is pissin' in a diaper bag.

The reason I'm in the jailhouse is all circumstantial evidence. They traced the croker sack to the mill. I ain't talking. "All circumstantial nonsense," my cousin-in-law the public defender says. Hell, I was fertilizing fields all day. Ten tons of nitrate on the ground to prove it. Cousin says I'll be out free and clear in a few days.

Wicker's old lady's a suspect now. A person of interest. She had the motive. He used to videotape hisself clubbing her, the bailiff told me. And she ain't liked it none neither. It wasn't no fun for her. He had hisself a video library of pain. He was one sick bastard.

They're going to drop the charges and release me come Friday morning, Judge Parnell says. Bond's been set at fifty grand for two weeks. Damn it all to hell. Judge wants me to train a squirrel dog for him. Hard as it is to get a good one right out of the bitch's ass. Think I'm going to find two half-brothers to Earl. Delbert Martin has the Treeing Feist stock Earl come from. I ain't going to name neither one of them till I can see which is the best. The best puppy I'm going to keep for my own self. Call him Earl Jr. And the other one I'll name Barabbas after a feller in the Bible. Let the judge have him and wash my hands of the whole damn thing. Live in peace for a while. Kill a few squirrel this winter.

ALL THE WAY TO FLORIDA
From *THE KING OF FLORA*
Michael Morris

The lights on the Catfish Pad sign had just begun to flicker. Neon yellow arrows pointed toward the restaurant. *All You Can Eat Catfish* sprawled across the marquee and the usual Friday night crowd answered the call.

Inside the cinder block building people filled green booths and an overflow of customers spilled across a lobby decorated with mounted fish, a plastic palm tree and a pinball machine that no longer worked. Chatter and clanging silverware rose up from air thickened by cooking grease. Waitresses dressed in white uniforms wove through the crowded tables while balancing trays of fried catfish platters and pitchers of iced tea.

My daughter, Imogene, pulled at my shirtsleeve. The wrinkles around her eyes deepened. "All this racket. Can we just get something to-go?"

"It'll do you good to be social. Now I want you to just keep your chin up and walk across that floor like you're as good as the next person."

Imogene darted to the corner and practically became one with the pinball machine with cracked glass. Nodding to the hostess I held up two fingers and pointed toward the dining room.

A touch of my arm caused me to turn and find Mattie Beckett. A Miss Alabama and first runner up in the 1968 Miss America pageant, Mattie still swatted her eyelashes whenever anybody brought up her past glory. Instead of clutching a bouquet of roses, she now cradled a grease stained take-out box. She bowed her head and rolled her dark eyes up at me. "I'm so sorry I couldn't make it to Clarence's funeral. I had that flu bug that's going around. How's Imogene managing?"

"It took some doing," I pointed toward the pinball machine where Imogene stood, "but I finally managed to get her out of the house."

Mattie put her hand on my forearm. "So good to see you. I'd love to see more of you." She squeezed my forearm and electrified me into believing I was a younger man.

Watching Imogene pull at the sleeves of her blazer while Mattie made polite conversation with her, I couldn't decide if it was inferiority or the scandalous way in which Clarence died that made Imogene so fidgety. Naturally, Mattie knew the circumstances the same as everybody else in the restaurant. The townspeople still waltzed around scandalous details the same way they had back in the days when Mattie wore her crown.

"Sheriff Gene, we're ready for you," the hostess said.

As I escorted Imogene through the crowd, diners turned with paper napkins clutched between their fingers and watched us. I pleasantly nodded but silently cussed the day that Clarence Posey slithered underneath my front door. A half-illiterate maintenance man who just happened to meet Imogene the one time her only girlfriend persuaded her to go to the skating rink in the middle of a weekday when no one would be there.

Imogene and I ended up seated at a corner table next to the latticework that separated the dining room from the area where the kitchen help congregated to refill soft drinks and pitchers of tea. While we looked over a menu, waitresses giggled behind the latticework. Their clipped conversation tangled with the sounds of dishes being stacked. Never seeming to notice us, the girls continued to squeal and gossip behind the lattice. Popping the menu open and coughing extra loud, I made a mental note to talk to the owner about their conduct.

"What're you having?" I leaned toward Imogene as she sheepishly scanned the room without turning her head. "I said what looks good to you?"

She quickly flipped the menu open and buried her head down, running her finger along the page.

Voices carried behind the lattice work. "I know one thing, if I ever catch my man with a woman that'll be the last time 'cause he won't be able to walk straight," said the youngest waitress.

"Just like that man that runs the junkyard off Highway 49. You heard about that? Girl, he was caught with that lady who tends the bar down by the county line. You know the one that likes to wear battery lights wrapped around her jacked up hair at Christmas time? Well that ole gal must've put a charge in him because the man had a stroke right in the woman's bed."

"Nah-uh…"

"I ain't joking."

"Wait. I heard something about this. Ain't his name…"

"Clarence Posey," the older waitress added.

Trying to stand and reprimand them, I knocked the chair out from under me. It tumbled against the table behind us just as a man was biting into a piece of fish. The woman with him yelped as the man's arm landed in a bowl of coleslaw. Before I could offer an apology, I saw Imogene's eyes twitch and her mouth quiver.

The girls' voices seemed to rise higher and stronger than the chatter of the catfish eaters. I pictured everyone in the restaurant standing over us, laughing and pointing.

"Clarence Posey. I seen him one time at the County Line Lounge dancing with Wynette. And her with them Christmas lights just a dangling in her hair. I reckon she shocked him good."

Throwing the menu to the floor, Imogene spun out of her chair never realizing that she had knocked over the vase of plastic daisies on the table. A waitress carrying a tray of food swerved to miss her but Imogene never looked back. She just walked faster, weaving around the clumps of people in the restaurant lobby.

When I finally made it outside Imogene was pacing the edge of the river, circling one of the oak trees. The doctor had told us long ago to let Imogene breathe inside a paper bag whenever her nerves got keyed up. Many were the nights that she was taken to the hospital with the declaration of a heart attack. "High strung," the doctor had called my daughter.

While citizens of Flora gossiped about the girl who hid behind the walls of our home, my wife Virginia continued to line the school books on the kitchen table and review the lessons that the teacher would drop off at the front door. Imogene's senior year of high school became a tiny planet with only her old friend, Hope Hullnet, as the lone alien granted a visa for weekly visitations.

Standing by the discolored boardwalk that ran behind the restaurant, Imogene balled her fist and made a face like she was fixing to scream but nothing came out.

"Just breathe now. There you go, take deep breaths." I moved slowly, the same way I'd do if she had a loaded gun.

A piece of moss attached and dangled from her shoe. The eyes that had seemed dazed from pills were now wide with an unrecognizable passion.

"Sugar, I'm going to go get you a bag to breathe in. So stay right here," I whispered. But before I could back up more than three steps the words began to flow as she stared off at the highway.

"You don't know how many times I've sat on my doorstep looking down that highway. Right after it rains the steam rises up off the pavement. Rises straight up in the air like it's hiding something. How far does it go?"

I whispered the same way her mama used to do. "What, baby?"

"The road. How far does it run?"

"Runs all the way to Florida."

She didn't try to pull away when I massaged the sleeve of her jacket. The material felt gritty and I clamped harder until I felt the sharp bone of her wrist.

"One day I'm going to head down that highway and never look back," she mumbled. If she would have spoken the words louder I might have believed her.

Pulling her closer, I closed my eyes and pictured a tube, similar to the one that had kept Clarence alive in the hospital, connecting me with Imogene.

A breeze flowed in off the river and moss danced from the oak limbs. Imogene placed her head on my shoulder and wrapped her arm around my waist. She gripped me until I wobbled to the side, almost falling. I leaned against the tree and Imogene leaned on me. The tree bark pressed and gnawed at my side. I steadied her and cast my gaze toward the summer steam that rose up from the highway like a haint, the ghost of Clarence Posey lingering over us.

SYNCOPE
Lynn Pruett

For three minutes, Lila endured the male nurse's clumsy probing of her forearm as he tried to find a fat vein. Then she passed out. When she came to, a cheerful female nurse with a flawless complexion was saying, "I have vasovagal syncope, too. It's an inherited condition. We just imagine a needle prick and over we go." The nurse laughed. "Now that I can see the color of your eyes, I have to try again or no colonoscopy."

"Do I have a choice?"

The nurse patted Lila's bruised inner elbow. "Of course not."

Lila's skin prickled all over and she took in a deep breath and turned her head away from the image that triggered her fainting. If the sight of a needle caused vasovagal syncope, would the nurse pass out, too? What a ghastly career choice for the cheerful woman, who was probably lying. Lila felt the stick and clamped her teeth and eyelids down.

"Finished. The doctor will be here shortly." The nurse's shoes swished across the floor.

Lila opened her eyes. The light was too bright but her quick tears distorted what she saw. A bulging curtain, a surgeon's table of steel instruments. The IV was in. She had not fainted. A small triumph that might lead to a bigger one? Beating an inherited condition? She hoped, prayed for a negative score on this test. She would not tell anyone, not even Dwight, her husband, who was out of town at a convention and did not know about the procedure, unless she had a reason to.

The curtain was drawn back. The doctor stood before her in a white coat and comfortable shoes.

Lila's eyes widened. She recognized him, though now he was older, thinner. Her blood rose to her face. Would the IV fluid pinken as well? She could feel heat along her neck. Him!

Maybe he would not recognize her. She was blond now, more filled out. The name on her chart, Maria Hargadine, was her first name and maiden name, but she was known by her middle name and married name as Lila Lesperance. Surely Maria Hargadine and Lila Lesperance were different people.

He read over her chart. "You are a little young for this."

"Family reasons," she said. "A little precaution in case the symptom is a symptom."

"You will be out for the procedure. You won't remember it."

"Good."

He tilted his head and gazed at her. "Did you write a book?"

Horrified and helpless, hooked up to the IV, she vacillated between honesty and dignity. He would see her big soft ass naked, he would look deeper inside her than anyone ever had. Her color deepened. She named its title.

"I bought that book. It was very good." He seemed pleased that he had guessed right. "And you wrote another."

She nodded and cursed the newspaper for its publicity, publicity she had cajoled from the editor. Though she fanned herself with her free hand in a gesture of dismissal, the doctor stood at the foot of her bed as if puzzling over why he would have bought her book and kept up with her career.

"Our sons were on the Storm soccer team together," she said, but declined to name her son. Why embarrass him? "Your son Bracque, how is he?"

The doctor's head dropped. "Bracque did Teach for America after college." His voice was resigned, even shy in offering this information, as if it contained a great shame.

"That's quite a worthy thing to do," said Lila, who was a teacher.

"Yes. Now he's an assistant principal in Watts." Again, the doctor mumbled and then squared his shoulders, preparing to defend this absurd career choice although he clearly did not approve of it.

Lila sat up straighter. Her knowledge of Watts was limited to reports of riots, Rodney King, and Olympic hurdler Kevin Young, which was no real knowledge at all. In fact, at the moment she questioned the sources of all her knowledge. What did she know about anything? Life, God, goodness, health? She forgot the man at the foot of her bed. Were these in fact her last minutes of blissful ignorance? Was she about to gain knowledge she did not want?

She faced the doctor who was now blush-colored, waiting for her judgment. What knowledge did she have of him? His perfect home in the gated neighborhood where they held a soccer cook-out. He'd been the booster club's president and his elegant wife the one mother who could cheer without sound. She read in the doctor's slumped posture the cost of personal achievement. His high expectations had been pressed onto his only son. (Lila was blessed with three sons, three opportunities for bragging. Or not.) Was a son who turned his back on high achievement and prestige worse than a colonoscopy performed by someone you knew?

If she was her sister Martha, she'd rub this in. She'd ask what the doctor wanted his son to become and would tsk-tsk over the idea of settling for teaching in a place with little reward, except maybe a spectacular, nationally-covered death, (fame!) with the silver lining being that these days any school anywhere was vulnerable to young lunatics with guns.

Instead, Lila considered what she would say. His was a parental fail in a family that did not fail. Yet in some circles, perhaps some she ran in—her whole life was spent running in circles—even now her mind circled back to the idea of Watts. Some parents would see Watts as a badge of honor. A son who was an assistant principal in Watts might trump a son who went to the Air Force Academy. Thank God she had a mind that ran in circles because the situation of the hospital bed, vasovagal syncope, bodily intrusion seemed unreal. She wanted to scream at the absurdity of this moment: I might have cancer and I'm presented with a problem of social intercourse. What kind of cosmic joke is this? Her fucking manners rose to the occasion to salve the doctor waiting for her to give a benediction or to call down a curse. "I remember that Bracque is likable and smart. I bet he will be a good role model for the students. People like Bracque should become teachers."

She lay back and thought, he looks into people's colons all day. Which end would you rather deal with? Bracque had made a better choice. How did her appointment become about him? Maybe it's easier to talk about those with a future than those of us who might not have one at all? Oh my sons, she almost cried out.

"Thank you for asking about Bracque," he said with a sincerity that touched her as true. "The nurse will bring the medicine and you won't remember a thing."

He left and the competent male nurse came back in and changed the IV bag with ease. She remembered the doctor had seemed so fine, the whole family had. They were beautiful people. Bracque was a soccer star racing down a bright green field under a night sky, the lights coating the players with the sheen of temporary glory, and the play she still remembered, seven headers in a row that moved the ball eighty yards for a score.

Those boys. When you're young you think you're exceptional. Even though you recognize treachery in the terrain, you think you will find the golden path—because you are exceptional. Then you cross the dark side of the mountain and step over into the sunlight and the bright side teems with so many, many million, exceptional people. This expectation of extraordinary must take a hit, and yet the insistent cry: I am still special. I will not get shot in Watts. My son will succeed me. I will not die of the disease that took my father. The voices clanged against each other like forks hung as a wind chime.

Then quiet, a dreamy perfect silence, the kind of floating she had longed for daily amidst the clatter of it all, the voices of children and angry men, the slamming doors, the rumble of the van, the shriek of the mother-in-law, the shrill excited barks of Fuzz every time the mailman shoved mail through the mail slot . . . none of that here. Why, none. She'd been Lila Lesperance, slightly off-stage, but now, now she would be the star of her own life.

160

BIRDS OF A FEATHER
Abbott Kahler

I have never wanted children, but I've always wanted birds—a
realization that dawned in December 1997 in the unlikeliest of places:
Las Vegas's MGM Grand casino, where my husband and I were cele-
brating our first wedding anniversary. One afternoon, in between rounds
of $5 blackjack, I wandered to a lobby and discovered a long perch sup-
porting a dozen parrots—scarlet and hyacinth macaws, cockatoos, and
lilac-crowned Amazons among them—riotous bursts of red and blue
and yellow and green, a preening, chirping string of jewels. I'd owned
birds since childhood, a succession of mild, low-maintenance para-
keets, beginning with a pastel beauty named Jake who rested on the
wire rim of my 1980s orthodontic headgear. But parrots were different
beasts, exotic and unpredictable. And some breeds have a life span of
sixty to eighty years. A parrot, I thought, could outlive us both.

That spring I visited a bird farm in suburban Philadelphia.
In hay-lined wooden squares resembling those at a farmers market
lay squirming piles of baby birds, eyes barely open, their skin goose
bumped where feathers were just beginning to grow. This time I was
drawn not to the colorful birds but to a bin of African grays, all a soft
shade of slate, their budding crimson tails the only splash of color.
There was something appealing about their faces, the way the chelo-
nian slope of their heads joined with their majestic black beaks; they
seemed solemn and dignified, the Mount Rushmores of the subfamily
Psittacinae. One of them was more restless than the others, determined
to be noticed. She waddled her way toward me, using nascent wings for
leverage, and fit herself into my palm. Through her tissue-paper chest
her heart flailed wildly against my skin.

I had promised my husband I would look but not buy. We were
twenty years old, had just bought our first house, and owed a combined
$100,000 in student loans. The bird cost $1,500, not counting cage,
formula, and toys, and required a nonrefundable $500 deposit. I lifted
her close to my face. Struggling, she managed to pry one obsidian eye

fully open and met my gaze. I named her Poe, after the writer.

Poe required vigilant care, as all babies do. We fed her with a syringe, heating the formula to a precise 103 degrees Fahrenheit, watching her chest—now dusted with dander—fill like a helium balloon. She burbled and chirped as I rubbed the sides of her beak. "Really?" I asked her. "Tell me more." A few months later she uttered her first word. "Really?" she asked in a slushy version of my voice. "*Really?*"

I had followed the research of Dr. Irene Pepperberg, whose groundbreaking work with an African gray named Alex upended long-held tenets about animal intelligence. Alex was a veritable avian genius, with a vocabulary of one hundred and fifty words and an advanced level of cognition; he wasn't merely imitating human speech, Pepperberg argued, but understanding it. Although I had neither the time nor the expertise to train Poe with such rigor, I was convinced she had the same potential for thoughtful communication. After mastering a word or phrase through mimicry, she used it in perfect context. "Want some juice!" she sometimes called, adding a gulping noise, an order to fetch orange juice. "Wanna go back" was a command to return her to her cage. "Good morning! Good morning!" she yelled until I got out of bed, then followed with a laugh that sounded exactly like my own. On long days working at home I sometimes treated her like a therapist, confiding my various frustrations. "Oh, shit," she said, cocking her head. And then: "It's okay, buddy. It's okay. I love you."

With this intelligence and seeming empathy came equally human neuroses, which worsened over time. Poe loathed the color purple; a certain pair of socks evoked prolonged cries of terror that sounded like grinding brakes. She flung unwanted food at walls and sometimes refused to eat at all. She marked the bathroom as her territory, growling and attacking our feet if we tried to enter. A veterinarian prescribed Prozac, instructing me to mix a few drops into her water—a successful solution until she detected the medicine. From then on, she dipped her tongue into water to test for bitterness before she drank. She began to pluck her feathers, the avian version of trichotillomania, leaving long strips of her torso bare and bloody.

"Please tell me what's wrong," I begged her, stroking her head. Pets were supposed to quell anxiety, but she had the opposite effect on me; I worried that my anxiety was another thing she'd learned to mimic, until she'd internalized it and made it real.

For once she had nothing to say. We decided that our pet needed a pet and bought Poe her own African gray. Dexter was the anti-Poe: plump and mellow, undiscerning in his appetites, content to sit and delicately preen his feathers, which were intact and flawlessly scalloped. He could mimic any household or street noise with tonal precision—the low-battery alert on our smoke alarm, the garbage truck driving in reverse—but was too lazy to bother with words. He was well suited to Poe, by which I mean he withstood her abuse without protest. When they sat side by side on their feeding stand, she crept over and nudged Dexter off. "Whoops, sorry buddy," Poe said, peering down, following this with her evilest laugh.

Poe liked having another member in the flock, though, especially one who was beneath her in the hierarchy. One summer Dexter flew away, disappearing into the woods behind our rental house. We spent six frantic hours searching for him while Poe remained uncharacteristically calm. "Come here!" she called again and again, punctuating this with a high-pitched shriek. Eventually, from deep in the woods, the shriek reverberated back. We found Dexter resting sleepily on a high branch, as though he'd just awakened from a long nap.

Dexter was an antidote but not a cure. Poe still plucked feathers the moment they took root; her little legs were bald. But no one had any answers. One evening in February 2016 I came home and took her from her cage. She sat on my lap, wilting like a flower in the heat, her breath coming in wheezy gasps. I called my husband to rush home. "It's okay, buddy," I told her, mimicking her words. "It's okay."

At the animal hospital she was placed into an "oxygen box," a small clear contraption she was to sleep in overnight. We were allowed to say goodbye to her. With great effort she said, simply, "Come here." We did. I tapped the glass and told her she was too stubborn to die.

During her exam the following morning, she did, her final defiant act. She had just turned eighteen, a baby in parrot years. The cause was heart disease, nearly impossible to detect in birds.

Dexter can't understand what happened to his friend of fifteen years, but he knows the flock has changed irrevocably. Sometimes he'll glance at Poe's spot on the feeding stand, as if waiting for her to appear and shove him off. "Who do we miss?" I'll ask him, and he says the one word he speaks with effortless clarity: "Poe."

IT'S BEEN SIX MONTHS
Pia Z. Ehrhardt

I'm visiting my neighbors on their shaded front porch. Retired AP reporters, they love to chat about books and local politics. They pour me a mug of delicious, dank chicory coffee, and Ella, our black Lab mix, makes herself at home. She's thirteen now. She was mostly my husband Malcolm's but since he died, she's become only mine. When a male pit bull passes by, I restrain her, hold her like a hug, until he's out of smell range. He's a mix of colors with a coat as thin and tight as a pig's. I have a friend who owns a pig, and she loves him like a dog, like a pet cat, like the named chickens she keeps in her backyard uptown: Henrietta, Margarita, Rosalie. Who watches this menagerie when she needs to travel, or to spend the night out? Who will watch Ella when I need to do these things? I am new at loss. The pit bull's owner, a muscular young guy, is letting the dog pull him down our block. Is it even in a pit bull to concede power? I fear Ella would lunge for this dog, lose her head and fight over her weight. Otherwise, she lives gently, so passively that sometimes I want to coach her up, tell her to quit waiting for commands, take a chance.

Losing a spouse opens the day up. I'm more friendly, available, without the distraction of marriage. Malcolm used to stick to hellos from a distance when I would've been okay with the halving: me drinking coffee on the neighbor's porch; him cutting grass or tending to his hedges before heading inside for a siesta.

Ella presses herself against their legs, giving them each a chance. Their son, in his fifties, lives at home. In college, he majored in Medieval literature. He so brims with esoterica that I want to take notes. For years, he's fed Ella treats through the fence; with the barrier gone, she's working him. We are talking about Moby Dick which I'm reading for the first time since my college attempt doesn't count. In their eighties now, the parents quote passages, and I envy their razor-sharp memories. I envy their doting marriage and that they will have had each other for many years longer than I had Malcolm.

Ella pees on flowering bindweed in their yard. I scold her back, but the neighbors consider this watering; besides, it's a weed, a pretty one with papery lavender flowers.

A troop of squeaky schnauzers passes by. To get to Ella, they tangle up their leashes, delighting their owner, a woman I also now know better. She trains physical therapists. She trained the PT who helped Malcolm after his knee surgery. He marveled at my husband's progress and strength, called him a rockstar, which inspired Malcolm. Things were going so well. My darling man, newly retired, on a pain-less space age knee, with a fine chunk of life still left to divvy up with errands, coffee and the newspaper in the morning, cocktails at night, cigars, travel. With our kids raised, we two were free birds.

Ella can't get through the mess of schnauzers although she'd love a butt scratch from their mom. She lives apart from her spouse, and they share dog custody; between them there are seven, eight, depending on which pups are able and alive. The two of them mix and match which dogs visit when. This batch moves too quickly to count. Five or six? I've heard that owning one schnauzer is cruel because they can't bear loneliness.

If dogs didn't live so long, I'd have another. There's dog-love left in me, unspent. Is there unspent man-love left in me? It's been six months since Malcolm died, and I'm in a no-man's land of shock and sadness and inertia. Unspent man-love used to branch through me like errant, wishful tributaries, water jumping the banks of the river that is marriage. It's useless to imagine possible men when your true man is gone. Ella will never love anyone as much as she loved Malcolm. When a blood clot raced from his leg to his heart, I was out of town. It was Ella who crouched beside him all day, loyal, a black sphinx, certain he was gone, but not giving up on her morning walk in the park, the af-ternoon kibble in her bowl; patient, alert, until a son stopped by in the evening to check on his too-quiet dad, and discovered what Ella knew. How do dogs recover the loss of their favorite person? How will I?

How will living with me be enough? Ella noses open the front door to find the neighbors' son who's gone inside to watch premier soccer on a small TV in the kitchen. He stores tasty bits of hope in the pocket of his shirt. He's easy to wear down. Treats help.

166

THE WORLD'S GREATEST PANTS
Michelle Richmond

About the time she entered ninth grade, Darlene acquired a steadfastness my parents found insulting. They labeled her defiant, but in my eyes she was brave. During her sophomore year of high school, I came upon Darlene and my mother in the kitchen, their faces not two inches apart, Darlene shouting, "If I were old enough to vote I'd cast my ballot for Jimmy Carter, just to cancel you out." She might as well have confessed to a murder.

Every moment between the two of them was a confrontation. I think our mother could not comprehend a daughter who refused to be intimidated, a daughter who refused to wear makeup. Darlene was kicked out of Girls in Action, the Baptist version of the Girl Scouts, for complaining that the Royal Ambassadors got to do "all the fun shit." She ran track at school and didn't shave her legs. When she skipped senior prom to go see *Platoon* with one of her track mates, my mother expressed aloud for the first time her concern that Darlene might be funny. "I'm beginning to think you might be funny," were her exact words.

"Funny as in ha-ha?" Darlene said, propping her feet on the kitchen table.

"There's nothing ha-ha about being funny," our father interjected from the living room. He was watching the Weather Channel. A hurricane was chugging toward the Gulf Coast like a sluggish locomotive, and he was excited.

Twenty minutes later I found Darlene in the back yard, sitting under the big oak tree with Baby, who was six years old that year. They were playing tic-tac-toe in the dirt, using acorns for playing pieces.

"Are you half acorns or whole acorns?" I asked Darlene.

"Half." She didn't look up, but I could hear in her voice that she was crying. Her shoulders shook slightly, and she kept her face turned toward the ground. I sat down beside her and said the only thing I could think of—

"I play winner."

"What's wrong?" Baby said. She started to cry too. Then Celia came outside. That was the year she got two hours a day out of her brace, and she looked relaxed and elegant, so slender I envied her. She sat down in our circle. By that point I was crying.

"What's wrong with everybody?" Celia asked.

"Mom called Darlene funny," I said.

Our mother came outside with the camera. "Smile," she said. "I want to get a picture of all my girls together."

Darlene left home a few months later. She staged a departure so bold and unexpected that anything the rest of us would later do seemed insignificant in comparison. She showed up one evening in January with a small girl in red vinyl pants so shiny they looked as if they'd been waxed at the car wash. The girl drove an old blue El Camino and wore eyeglasses with big black frames. She stood the way girls stand in movies when they're about to do something rash, looking bored, explosive, and sex starved all at once. When we went out to greet them in the driveway, the girl slid her arm protectively around Darlene's waist.

"This is Beth," Darlene said, looking at Celia instead of my mother. "We've got a place in Bandera."

"Cool," Celia said.

My mother, at last, turned to me. "Where's Bandera?" she asked.

"Texas, maybe?"

Beth nodded and offered proudly, "It's the dude ranch capital of the world. My parents have some land."

"How many acres?" my mother asked, temporarily gaining her composure. Up until that moment, I think she held out some hope that Darlene would someday be a bride.

"Fifty," Beth said. I could almost hear my mother's mental calculator ticking off the land value.

Daddy had been standing by the back door, watching. "If you stay at home we could pay for you to go to the university," he said. Money was tight, but he was serious.

"Thanks," Darlene said, "but we've already decided."

"You don't even have to live with us," Daddy said. "Just stay in Mobile and we'll work everything out. We'll find you an apartment." Beth caught my eye and winked, like we were in on this together. I was embarrassed to have her witness my father's awkward desperation.

Beth helped Darlene load some clothes into the El Camino, while our parents stood by, silent. Baby wanted to know if she could come too. Celia and I promised to visit, and Daddy said quietly that we would do no such thing. When they were ready to go, my mother wrapped her arms around Darlene and held on so tight I thought we'd have to pry her fingers loose. "Mom," Darlene said. "It's just Texas."

When Beth reached out to shake my mother's hand, Mom folded her arms across her chest and backed away. "Just remember she's been my daughter for eighteen years," she said. "You can't change that."

Daddy stood under the carport, looking shocked and powerless, his arms hanging at his sides. "When are you coming back?"

"As soon as you invite us," Darlene said.

Later, Mom called Celia and me to the dining room table. "What I want for all of my girls is a comfortable situation, happiness, and a moral life," she said. "It is possible to have all three."

That night in bed I thought of Darlene and Beth in the shabby El Camino, driving through Texas, which must be as dark as it is big. I was filled up with pride for Darlene, who was old enough and strong enough to leave us. I thought of my sister with her hand on Beth's thigh, how those red vinyl pants would be warm beneath her fingers. I closed my eyes and remembered the world's greatest pants, and I fell asleep dreaming of that deep and miraculous shine.

THE GREEN WOMAN
Janet Nodar

One night, Lisa dreamed that her well-groomed but fly-away hair began to pump out of her scalp and thicken and twist like wisteria vines around the mattress, the pillows, the bedposts. Her fingernails and toenails burst forth from her feet and fingers. They hooked their way across the carpet and up the drapes with little snaffling tendrils. Her hands and feet burned. Her shaved armpits burned. The cleft between her legs burned. Her vining body cinched her into the bed like a gnat in a web. Lisa knew she was only dreaming, but her heart was pounding against her ribs.

When the alarm went off at 6:15 the bedroom was cool and dark, the jacquard bedspread only mildly disturbed. Jack, her husband, was whistling in the shower. Lisa arranged the pillows, pulled back the silky curtains. She made pancakes for breakfast and then helped her son review for a chemistry exam. She glanced at herself occasionally in the mirror over the polished sideboard. She looked much as usual, a slender woman in dark slacks and a soft blue wrap-front blouse. A tinny mental residue, like the after-taste of diet cola, was all that remained of her dream.

At her office desk later that morning it struck Lisa that her fingers looked peculiar. Greenish. She went outside to examine them in daylight. It was only her imagination. Fluorescent lights made everything look sickly. She did ask the opinion of a co-worker standing nearby, however.

"Fluorescent lights," he agreed, cigarette smoke curling out of his nose.

She thanked him, and he nodded. Glad to help. She looked at her hands again. It all seemed like a trick.

On Saturday, Lisa dozed off in a wicker chair in the backyard. When she woke, she couldn't move. She strained to shift her feet. It was as if roots had sprouted from her heels and knitted her into the ground. The sun burned down on her nose and arms and made her eyes water. The humid air filled her lungs. She could hear the fountain tinkling, smell pine straw. Was it a stroke? A spell? Who could have done this to her?

But no— her children were calling her. Their voices plugged her back together. She moved her arms and legs. She stretched, gratefully.

Later that afternoon, Lisa put her house plants—ferns, devil's ivy, philodendron, coleus—outside. She'd let the caterpillars eat them. Who cared? The lawn was as green as lime Kool-Aid. In bed at night she could sense it simmering outside her window, breathing, waiting. In the Southwest, where she had once lived, lots of people didn't bother with lawns. They just burned off the weeds once a year and spread sparkling gravel in their yards. Jack was a little irritated with her when she mentioned this to him a second time. No one had a sparkling gravel yard in Mobile, Alabama. The neighbors would think they were crazy. Besides, he enjoyed his riding lawn mower. Lisa bought a twenty-pound sack of salt, and when Jack wasn't home she sprinkled handfuls of it over the lawn and in the flower beds. The hydrangeas shriveled. The lawn turned gray and brown. Poisoned. Serves you right, she thought.

One day Lisa's daughter suggested that she get a checkup. "Better safe than sorry, Mom," she said. So Lisa made an appointment. The doctor tapped and listened and took samples. She was fine. For fun, she made an appointment with a psychiatrist. She wrote up some preliminary notes: *My parents were marvelous people. We adored each other. We lived in a lovely house in a pleasant, tree-shaded suburb. We had a maid named Nora. We spent our summers at Point Clear. I rode my bicycle on the concrete streets. I watched the same cartoons as everyone else. I sang in the choir at church and I rode horses.*

Honestly, Lisa had never been unusual. She had never wanted to be. It seemed important to stress this during her session with the psychiatrist, to make him see that she should not be faulted. They spoke politely to one another. She answered his questions and pondered his deck of pictures. He rubbed his dimpled chin and wrote her a prescription. Lisa could not tell if she'd made her point.

The medicine made her feel as if her skull was stuffed with cottage cheese. She took it seven times and then buried the pills in the spot where the biggest hydrangea had been. That seemed to help. Her concerns lifted for a time. Her son became engaged to a charming girl and her daughter was awarded a scholarship to a prestigious college. As a test, Lisa put an African violet in her bedroom. She never watered it, and the room was always dim, but it flourished anyway. Then one morning Lisa parted her hair and saw that her scalp was covered with a pale, sinuous pattern of leaves and stems and purple flowers.

She dropped the comb. What an enemy she had! It almost pleased her, the slyness of her foe. She imagined her autopsy, the pathologists cutting her open and marveling at the creature twined within her. She snipped the African violet to pieces with her kitchen shears and pruned her hair down to her skull. The pattern receded.

A few days later, Jack had a heart attack while fretting over his gardening catalogues. They decided to downsize and quickly sold the house for a handsome profit in spite of the ruined lawn. They moved to a condo. Lisa painted all of the rooms white. She really wanted to move somewhere flat and cold, a scoured place where nothing grew and she could see all the way to the horizon, but her husband would never agree and she didn't want to go alone, so she compromised. Lisa drove back and forth to work, averting her eyes from the trees.

She thought it wisest not to let her hair grow back. Jack eventually quit asking her why. He told people she was a terrorist. She covered her slick head with a scarf. Strangers spoke to her gently, assuming she had cancer. Although she didn't correct them, she didn't feel that she was cheating. After all, something treacherous multiplied in her. A moment's carelessness, and what green riot would ensue?

WHAT I KNOW NOW
THAT I WISH I'D KNOWN THEN
Cassandra King

I was twenty-five when I cut my wisdom teeth. My mother, never at a loss for a proverb, was appalled. "Folks used to say," she warned me, "that when you cut wisdom teeth, you've lived half your life." Had that old superstition held up, I would've died at fifty. I didn't. And I made it safely (more or less) past sixty and seventy. Now, like all old people, I look back on my twenty-year-old self with a mixture of fondness, horror, and regret. I would not go back to being twenty-five again for the world. Matter of fact, my worst nightmare is that one day a fairy godmother will appear with a magic wand and transport me back to my youth. In case it ever happens, though, I'd want to be better prepared this time. So here are ten things I know now that I wish I'd known then:

1. ***Actions have consequences***. I thought I could skip studying chemistry and pass it anyway. I thought I could have unprotected sex and not get pregnant. No matter how reckless my behavior, I thought I could make my excuses to some understanding, forgiving deity and everything would be okay. I failed to see that *actions have consequences* isn't just a little ditty: it's a basic principle of nature, as true as the law of gravity.

2. ***You don't always get a second chance***. Related to number one, but not quite the same. It's about regrets for the life you meant to live, but somehow didn't.

3. ***Nothing hurts forever***. You get your heart broken and it hurts like hell. It hurts and hurts some more. Over time, the staggering pain becomes a dull ache. Next thing you know, the ache has become a dull memory. Trust me on this.

4. ***You can't die on every cross***. Pick your battles. In my youth, I thought I could save the world. That's because I foolishly thought the world could be saved.

5. ***Rainy days come***. And go.

6. ***Nobody dies of embarrassment, shame or fool-***

ishness. If so, I wouldn't have lived past twenty.

7. ***The body declines; looks go.*** I was once a cute little blonde, all one hundred pounds of me, which I took to the bank. I batted my lashes at traffic cops when I got pulled over for speeding; wore mini-skirts to male professors' classes hoping to get an A; flirted shamelessly with attached men at parties. Now I look in the mirror and realize there's some justice in the world after all.

8. ***Money is not a big deal.*** It's okay to spend it, save it, give it away, or worry over it. It's only money. It can be your friend, but it's not your enemy. The only enemy in life is time. Keep in mind, the last suit you wear won't need pockets.

9. ***Most things that cause us so much worry do not matter, do not matter, do not matter***. Repeat as often as needed.

10. *Fifty—or sixty or seventy or eighty—ain't so bad*. Not only that, they're much, much better than twenty-five. One day, you'll see what I mean.

PERMISSION
Bret Anthony Johnston

The owners had driven to their hunting lease for the weekend, but their daughter stayed home. Marnie was a vegetarian. After they left, she pulled the lever to drain her parents' new kidney-shaped pool. Then she texted Chase. "Gate's unlatched. Bring friends."

Chase and I skated together sometimes. His parents were doctors, like Marnie's, which is how he knew her. They were sixteen, two years older than me, and attended a Christian school. I didn't think we were real friends. It took an hour to skate to their neighborhood. My feet vibrated from all the pushing.

The pool was a dark flawless blue—elliptical transitions, rounded brick coping, stairs like a wedding cake. That first day our wheels streaked the plaster with chlorine dust, the tracks reminded me of jet contrails marring the sky. When I arrived the next morning, the walls were dripping with crimson spray paint—obscenities, mostly, and misshapen band logos. I figured Marnie would make us spend the weekend scrubbing graffiti, but she was in the shallow end painting a massive pentagram.

On Saturday afternoon, some kid snapped an ankle trying to boardslide the stairs. It sounded like a balloon bursting. After the ambulance departed, Marnie doused the coping with lighter fluid. Chase and I slashed frontside grinds through the flames. My shoes got charred. Strangers lay passed out on the deck that reeked of vodka puke. Leaving, I heard someone say: "Let's tattoo him!"

The gate was latched on Sunday. I couldn't hear anyone skating, but the front door was open. I rang the bell. I knocked. The Saltillo tile was mud-smeared; the air smelled of spent firecrackers. I wondered if Marnie was dead, if burglars had roped her to a chair while they bagged her mother's diamonds. I wiped my feet before entering. Creeping through the rooms, I expected to be assailed from behind. I clutched my skateboard like a bat.

Marnie was outside, legs dangling over the deep end. She wore slouchy velvet boots. She was refilling the pool with a garden hose. The water reached her heels. It undulated, caught the sun, and threw shimmering light in unexpected angles. I said, "Your front door's open."

"Parents will be here soon. I wanted them to feel welcome."

"I can help clean or—"

"Did you have fun?" she interrupted. "Was skating here less thrilling because you didn't have to hop a fence?"

"I like permission pools," I said. "You don't have to worry about getting busted."

"Permission," she said. "Sounds boring."

"You should call the cops next time," I said.

Marnie smiled like I had solved a riddle. She patted the coping: an invitation.

I put my board down, gave a single push, and rolled toward her. Marnie shifted the hose for me to sit by her side. Her boots were submerged now, ruined. I hung my feet over the edge, too.

A truck rumbled into the driveway. The engine shut off. One door opened and closed, then another. Marnie corrected her posture, raked her hair. When her father called for her in the house, she kicked off her boots in giddy excitement. Water sloshed over my charred shoes. Her father yelled her name. I sat up straight. Beneath the rippling surface, the graffiti was pulsing like blood from fresh wounds. Marnie's hand stole into mine. I squeezed.

NEVER-ENDING
Sydney Thompson

Cooper woke to a familiar craving: another yoga/dance stunt, like what Leah had accomplished the first time they had sex. How she, beneath him, kissing him, her arms squeezed around him, pulled his boxers down with her feet, then hooking her legs behind his and arching her back, now up on her elbows, she lowered him and guided him in. It was some magical combination of the Cobbler Pose and Fish Pose.

Listening to Leah's heavy breathing and the ticking of palm fronds, Cooper couldn't stop thinking of Trace and Tory. He'd always wanted to break into a house and fuck his girlfriend—or fuck his wife. Fuck someone. It was an old fantasy that returned to him over the years, and it did so again earlier that day, when he and Leah had viewed the yellow house on Willowbridge Lane, and then moments ago in a dream. He nuzzled up behind her. Feeling the cushion of her ass against his erection aroused him further, until he ached. He eased his arm around the slope of her waist, then cupped a breast through her pajama top. He hoped she might wake in a good emotional place and want a better emotional place, for their contact to persist and intensify and become love. Cooper refused to believe that desiring stasis had become her default setting. But she reflexively blocked him with her elbow and her deep breathing immediately resumed.

In college, he'd written a story about a teenage couple breaking into houses to have sex. Trace and Tory began with houses under construction, with doors but with no doorknobs, the young, passionate couple romantically humping nakedly in drifts of sheetrock powder and sawdust in the light of stars, then candles. They progressed to empty houses for sale with unlocked windows they could raise to let themselves in, and with carpeting and running water, and they'd plan ahead, taking wine and sliced apples and cheese, then in one scandalous scene a jar of creamy Peter Pan peanut butter.

Eventually, Trace and Tory broke into lived-in houses with plenty of equity, while the owners were away at work or on vacation.

They'd break a window or splinter a door frame and then would eat from the refrigerator, at times cooking elaborate meals, though other times they chose to feed the pets, or to play video games late into the night, until ultimately, by the end of the story, they stopped having sex and only broke into recently renovated historic homes to take naps in sheets with high thread counts. Cooper didn't know where to go with the idea from there.

SUCH IS MAN
Robert Gatewood

I hadn't been able to get out of bed for several days already, and that morning felt no different. Gina was in the kitchen cooking sausages. It had been a long morning for her, I know, getting up to make the sausages in hopes that I would smell them and come downstairs. Her face was screwed up in anger, I could see it, grinding the meat and stuffing it in the casings. This was when Gina was at her prettiest. Her nose grew even more slender and the shadows under her eyes widened and darkened. Beneath the tip of her nose her lips compressed into a little red mound, so that her whole face gave the impression of a scalpel poised over a throbbing wound. I never described it to Gina like this, of course. I would just tell her she looked like a Modigliani painting, a painter I knew by name only because Gina was born in Sicily and like all immigrants she fetishized the historical figures of her native country, a way to cope with the alienation that pours over you when American life is no longer a fantasy but a daily battleground.

But the scalpel and wound is what aroused me. Nothing seemed to stir my interest anymore unless it carried a suggestion of violence.

After a while I made my way down the stairs and into her little pocket of time and space. When a man is captive to a woman, he perceives that she commands a kind of provincial dominion within the time-space continuum. This is probably not a verifiable phenomenon, but such is man.

"You can take the girl out of the veal pen but you can't take the veal pen out of the girl," I said, hoping her anger might persist long enough to keep me in thrall.

"There's no need to be cruel," she said.

Unfortunately she seemed quite calm, and just like that the moment had passed.

"Ah but if beauty be cruel, then so must cruelty be beautiful."

Gina turned from her little butcherblock island and slashed the

air with a knife. "You know there's nothing I despise more than gratu-
itous poetry. Anyway I use pork and beef."

This had been the very first thing that attracted me to Gina,
this peasant's directness. Even under the strain of my condition not
once had she modified her treatment of me. She had an instinctive
understanding that the only cure for poverty, in whatever form it appeared, was ruthless economy.

"I'm sorry. I don't know what's wrong with me. Maybe we
should get a dog."

"What for? We already have you to piss on anything that's pretty."

It was true. I had ruined everything. You have to be careful
with cynicism. Fool around with it too long and it can soften and spread
and before you know it, it has become a personal philosophy.

"You're right," I said, and retreated to the window. There was
no sun but there was a glare on everything, like a brass band playing.
"I'm sorry. Us Botzenhardts are slow healers. I feel like we've been over
all this. Listen, it's not you, it's me. Do you believe me?"

"Yes."

"Or maybe it's not. It's like this. Love is patient and patience is
a virtue. On the other hand, wait around long enough and you'll find
out there's nothing love won't destroy. It's a puzzle, I swear."

Gina slid a tray of sausages into the oven and yanked the ban-
danna out of her hair. It spilled down her shoulders like squid ink, so
black you could almost believe it wasn't real.

"I think that's kind of the point," she said.

I picked up the knife she'd put down on the counter and
examined the blade. How strange it is that you can't see the quality of
sharpness, I thought. You just know that it's there.

"I don't think you can imagine what it's like," I said.

"What what's like?"

"What do you mean, what what's like?"

"Well it's certainly hard for me to imagine."

I looked into her eyes. They were like moist glands unwilling to
secrete their meaning.

"That's a pretty sick joke," I said.

"Look, I just don't understand what you're trying to communicate exactly."

As usual, Gina had a point. Say what you will about clarity of purpose, but you have to admit there are certain situations when it can be helpful.

"What can I say?" I said, and sat down at the breakfast table. "Here's the church and here's the steeple and we've closed early for business. What the hell else is there to say?"

"Maybe it's a holiday."

"Yeah, right."

"Somebody's bound to come back and unlock the door."

"You'd like to think."

Gina had set the table for two, with her little napkins folded up like tents. I punched one down and chopped up the stick of butter with her knife. I could feel her watching me.

"People need to be able to pray," she said.

In my mind I opened it up and looked inside and felt the emptiness like you feel the wind, everywhere and nowhere all at once. I could barely bring myself to look at her.

"I don't know if this is going to work out," I said.

That's when she walked over to me and stopped the blade with her hand.

"No," she said, and squeezed.

Smoke was now escaping from the lip of the oven but still I could see that her nose had begun to aerate and her eyes were turning marvelously dark.

"No," she repeated, and tightened her grip with thrilling assertiveness. "So what are you going to do about it?"

It seemed like a very long time, a lifetime maybe, before I felt the livid heat of Gina's pulse in my hand, smelled the blood and the garlic, and all at once remembered what I had forgotten. "I'll do what I can," I said, and closed my hand over hers.

DISNEYLAND
Michelle Richmond

He takes six steps down the hallway to the living room, where he slaps the chandelier and it does its glassy rattle-tattle. On his shoulders I'm as tall as the sun, slippety-slap his head's a drum. My mother arrives. He sets me down. Celia walks in, head high, back straight, the metal buckles of her back brace clinking as she goes. Darlene lies across the sofa, struggling with a Rubik's Cube.

We've all been gathered here today, he begins. It sounds like a joke but my mother isn't laughing, the stuffing's coming out of the gold chair in the corner, the ferns in the planter box are dying. *Lordy*, he says. *Uh-huh*. He's a white man from Mississippi who sounds like a Ray Charles song.

One room over, Baby's in her crib. Mother has painted the room with clouds and sheep. She even built a white picket fence that stands knee-high around the room. *Beautiful, beautiful, angel mine*, Daddy says whenever he sees the baby. Still, he never holds her, never puts her on his shoulders, which leads me to believe that I am the best-loved girl.

Gotta go, he says, sing-song, but it's nothing from the radio. I know right off he means it. *It's not your mother's fault, we don't get along. I'll be back to visit.* Three steps from the gold chair to the door, eight from door to truck, where his shirts hang neatly on a rod. Everything's been planned. He backs slowly down the driveway, waving with a smile on his face like he's going to Disneyland.

THE THING WITH FEATHERS
Suzanne Hudson

She didn't meet her stepfather until she was five, having lived
with a cousin of her mother's in Beaumont, Texas, since she was born,
having been ensconced in the womb during the marriage ceremony.
An apathetic judge of probate oversaw the wedding, a hasty ritual her
mother rushed in order to find legitimacy for her daughter. And her
mother thought it best to spend some time alone with this man who
was now a husband, would be a husband for the next thirteen years,
until he shot himself in the head on a creek bank—accidentally, some
said; on purpose, said others.

The relative who brought her up to the age of five was sometimes affectionate but many times harsh, tugging at the child's clothing
in frustration as she dressed her, brushing, too hard, at the tangles in
the child's hair, impatient and full of spat-out sighs, like the sounds of
an angry cat. Still, there were storybooks read, in drowsy snuggles on
the relative's bed when it was time for a nap, and the soothing sound
of her surrogate mother's voice spun silky tendrils of hope, though she
couldn't name it at the time, throughout her spirit.

Her mother visited her on her birthdays, sent her packages at
Christmas time, doll babies in shiny wrapping paper tied up in fumbled
ribbon, shipped in boxes all bumpled and scarred by errant post-
masters. The child played with the dolls on the floor of the relative's
kitchen while boiling cabbage eked its humid, acrid scent into the walls,
the curtains, the sad, cheap furniture. Then one day she was told it was
time to go and meet her stepfather.

She remembered hanging back, there in the doorway of her
new parents' house, dropping her eyes from his overpowering form.
He was all plaid flannel shirts, khaki work pants, and heavy boots
that seemed to shake the earth. He worked to win her over, his fingers nibbling at her ribs, games played until he drew her in to the fun,
though she always glanced away, holding back a bit of herself. "She's

shy," her mother said, but she wasn't. So he called her "Sugar Bugger" and "Baby Doll" and "Dipsey Doodle." When he came in from work he would throw her in the air and the world would blur and she would shriek with delighted laughter, even though there was that quick moment of terror, breath sucked back and where was Jesus?

He had a shotgun for killing deer, limp brown forms laid blood-spotted in the bed of his truck on autumn evenings. He had a thick-handled, thin-bladed silver knife for slitting through the skins of squirrels and catfish, or carving through the meat of an apple to offer her a small slice: "Eat it down, Sugar Bugger. An apple a day keeps the doctor away." He had a pistol he would use sometimes at night, to shoot at the raccoons that dug in the garbage, crashing her awake, sending her crying to her mother, who would say, "Don't be silly. Go back to sleep. Your mama's tired as the devil."

He had a collection of fishing lures—rubber worms in purple and orange, golden spinners shimmering, enticing her—a kaleidoscope's colors, some like feathered jewels in the hinged, top-handled treasure chest he carried.

"Show me the thing with feathers, Daddy," she would say, for he had insisted that she call him "Daddy," and she, who had never had one, tried the word on and enjoyed the way the sound of it wrapped her in the feel of a safe-layered warmth.

"They ain't feathers," he would say, pulling out the shyster lure, letting her tickle it with the soft tips of her fingers. "Fish don't eat nothing with feathers."

He bought her a pair of burnt-red cowboy boots when she turned six, winning her loyalty to a ritual of replacement whenever she needed to size up. He played her country music songs on the car radio, ordered her a white-fringed cowgirl dress, and grinned large when she put it on. "You as pretty as Patsy Cline," he said.

"And spoiled as your soul," her mama said to the air.

He drank beer most of the time—like water, her mama said— and whiskey of an evening, and if the child was up too late she would sometimes see the other man emerge, the one who was much more unpredictable, the stumbling one, who mumbled curses and kicked her mother's bedroom door when she shut him out.

"Don't want no drunk slobbering over me," her mother would say.

He finally took her fishing when she was seven, a special day, just the two of them, to a pond that pooled a blue stain in the woods, where he cast into the weeds, building a mound of empty cans, with each toss of a can a glance at her, going from strange into threatening into frightening and her eyes chased for Jesus. Then, the pile of cans grown, when the sun caved in to the horizon, he twirled her hair around his fingers, stroked her face, her little arms without recourse because she didn't understand. And when he put his hand to her panties, the soft white cotton ones her mother hung out on the line each week to dry, the ones he would throw into the blue pond going all deep-colored as the sun withdrew, tears streaked trails of salt down her cheeks because it hurt and she wanted her mama.

In elementary school the child was not especially noticeable, moving at an average pace, producing average work, seeming good natured, even charming at times. But at home she had grown tense and vigilant, keeping alert, watching doorknobs, listening for the pad of feet down the hall, in the night, while her mama slept. She had to stay keen to the barometric changes in the atmosphere of the little house, because she knew that darkness held the syrupy smell of whiskey riding warm breaths across the slurred dreams of a girl now eight years old—when her only father would stand beside her bed and put her small palm to the thing that lived there beneath the hairy curve of his belly.

She would try to shove pictures into the grainy dark, try not to see him, not feel the mash of her tiny hand into his, but she could not pretend his looming form away or conjure anything that would color the shadows, not while she looked into the dark. So she shut her eyes so tight it hurt, sending bursts of light against her clenched lids. And all the while, as he moved her palm along the creature he coaxed with his own, she would see nothing but the bluebells growing along the highway, or yellow buttercups at Easter, or her mother's azalea bushes. She would bathe herself in floral colors, fending off the dark and the molding of her fingers to the creature taking shape there, boozy breaths bearing down on her small body. She strung the flowers into garlands spiraling around the little bed until his breaths hit hard and the thing spat venom across the pistons and velvet petals she had laced through the thick layers of the night.

When she was nine, ten, eleven, he would take her on long rides in the game preserve, slits in the rough-trunked horizon strobing sunlight, her sight on the edge of a look, a quick cut of an eye, never full-on and vulnerable, never a challenging stare. She would lean her chin on her hand and hang her arm out the open window, trying to catch and hold the air. Just the two of them, furtive, like lovers trysting and traveling across the borders of contexts and closed-off emotions. He would find hidden, high-walled creek banks, where he would fire his pistol at the empty beer cans that clattered across the bed of his pickup. He taught her how to shoot, wrapped her small fingers around the butt of the Ruger, helped her support the weight of it, showed her how to hold it, palm cupping wrist, breathe in, let out slowly, as shoulders drop, squeeze—no, no, squeeze, real slow, Baby Doll. That's it, that's it.

The noise of it, set off from her own thin fingers, crashed booming into the wild silence of the forest, an ear-ringing power that she could have never imagined, and its echo cracked and cracked its fade into a silence. She liked it. So she practiced, asked him to teach her how to load, clean and care for the thing, squealed with the thrill of firing it, exhilarated by its blasts, those sounds that had more than once chased her from her little bed. She made secret dares, vows to herself to get better, be the best, know it like an intimate friend, a confidante. In time she began to practice with more determination, with the grim focus of a guerrilla warrior, whenever he took her out for one of their rides down the red clay roads curling through the wooded walls that hid them. She put aim at beer cans and milk cartons and squares of cardboard with bull's-eyes drawn on them. She exploded an olive green wine bottle she had found under her mother's bed, sending a spray of glass bits sparkling like emeralds scattered to the sky.

"Got him!" her stepfather grunted.

And she smiled at him, a coy one, one she had learned to use early on, to maneuver him there in the unpopulated margins of her life. She could force an advantage, she had gradually discovered, could write a tune without words and suspend him in a dance. A lift of her chin, a pout of her lip, an inflection, a glance—she had found where

186

the lines could be, if she wanted them there. She could change the course of a day with the bat of a lash, the turn of a wrist, the knowledge she had filed away during those solitary moments at his side. She could finally see who might really hold the cards, and where his weaknesses resided, and get the true lay of the land he had hidden for so many years without her ever suspecting. She squeezed the trigger.

"Got him!"

And she knew she had. Even at the age of eleven, twelve, and then, thirteen, she knew she had "got him," would get him, eventually, Jesus or no. She would take it upon herself, still a child but not a child—never, really, a child. She would take herself up on her secret dare and look at him directly, for once, eyes focused hard down the barrel of a gun, silver and straight, its lines looming outward from her fixed gaze like railroad tracks, parallel until she inched it down, real slow, breathing out, the square of the sight put to the target at the end of her vision. She would meet him on a riverbank and burn him red, his work boots all slogged in the slick mud. She would get him and reclaim herself, take herself by her little girl's hand, dimpled and unscarred, to the place where her soul was hidden. And then, finally, the two of them would blend into each other, into the notes of the music, notes in chromatic half-steps and notes of modulation, staves winding around and nestling against the warm skin of the relative in Beaumont, Texas, where the thing with feathers could sit unabashed on its perch, reach into its sweet, sweet depths, and sing.

GONER
Beth Ann Fennelly

That Friday, after morning Mass, the priests visited our third grade to announce a meeting for prospective altar boys.

I went. Me, a girl. Why did I go? First, I was attracted to the pageantry: the costuming with the alb and the cincture, the procession with the cross and the thurible filled with incense. I wanted to arrange the credence table--the corporal, the cruet, and the ciborium. I wanted to raise the aspersorium of holy water into which the priest dipped the aspergillum before raining blessings on penitent heads. When he lifted the Eucharist, I wanted to twist the cluster of brass sanctus bells, alerting our souls to transubstantiation, bread and wine miracled into Body and Blood. And clearly I wanted to fill the chalice of my mouth with the wine of those words.

Also, I went to prove a point.

But I never got the chance. Before the meeting began, Father Mayer evicted me from the front pew. "I'll be right back," he told my classmates, then steered me by my shoulder to the sacristy where, behind a heavy door, a few old ladies bent over ironing boards. *The altar society*, he informed me, *cares for the priestly vestments. This is where God calls you to serve.* He fled, and I fled, and that evening in my best penmanship I tattled on him to Cardinal Joseph Bernadin. My letter ended, *P.S. And women should be priests!* My mom loved the letter: how cute, our little women's libber.

Now, a grown woman with children of my own, back in Illinois at my mother's table, I read in *The Trib* that Father Mayer sexually abused altar boys. For decades. He'd been removed from St. Mary's and sent to St. Edna's, removed from St. Edna's and sent to St. Stephen's, removed from St. Stephen's and sent to St. Dionysius', removed from St. Dionysius' and sent to St. Odilo's. All those altered boys. Did the archdiocese, the Cardinal, know? *Please.* In the church files, there's a contract Father Mayer signed, promising that at St. Odilo's he wouldn't be alone with boys under twenty-one. Because by then two of his altar boys had committed suicide.

After St. Odilo's, he was sent to jail.

You can look all of this up, if you care to. Father Robert E. Mayer, pastor of St. Mary's, Lake Forest, Illinois, 1975 to 1981. Call this fiction: I dare you.

I lay the newspaper down in a light that is no longer the light of my mother's kitchen, but is the stained light of St. Mary's, where solid pillars of dust propped up the clerestory windows, and in this light I see it all anew, I see it all anew, and clear as a bell, as we say, as if cued by altar boys twisting the sanctus bells, announcing that something has been transubstantiated into something else, forever. The ironing women who lifted the blank communion wafers of their faces. The click of dress shoes as Father rushed back to the meeting, his robes streaming behind him like wings. A year later, his sabbatical. His goodbye pot-luck.

My outrage at not being chosen. My bad luck at being born a girl.

My classmate Donny O'Dell, who *was* chosen, during Mass that unseasonably warm Easter—he was holding high the Bible, rigid and dutiful, when suddenly he toppled backward. The whole congregation heard the sickening thwack of skull on marble, and as one, we uttered the same surprised *Oh!*—as if it were part of the Mass, as if a response had been inserted before the Agnus Dei,—*Oh!* we cried, in a single voice—and how quickly Father was at his side, bending, lifting in his arms the small boy, Donny O'Dell, a boy even smaller than I was, Donny in his arms like Jesus removed from his cross, or, with his white alb flowing toward the floor, like a bride. And how Donny raised a hand to his head and opened his eyes and realized that he'd fainted and smiled sheepishly. How the parishioners laughed a relieved laugh to see he was okay. How the ushers led Donny outside into the fresh air. How later, filing out into the narthex, everyone laughed again with Mrs. O'Dell. *Your son gave us quite a scare, Nance. For a moment, we thought he was a goner.*

WELCOME TO MONROE
Daniel Wallace

On the morning of the seventh day you knew they'd never find
you. Not with dogs or with flashlights or with helicopters or handouts or
all the men and women from town walking in lines through the woods
so they wouldn't miss a thing. They would never find you because you
couldn't be found. You were far away by then, somewhere near Monroe,
Alabama. You knew that because that was the last sign you saw before
he turned off that long stretch of main road. *Welcome to Monroe.* And the
woods so deep and dark there, big enough to swallow the world. What
a time for something like this to happen, days before Christmas, so close
to Christmas that many of your presents were already wrapped and
waiting beneath the tree. But this Christmas would be different from
all the Christmases before it for your mother and your father and your
brother and everyone who knew them, knew you. At school the teachers
would take your friends aside and ask them questions, and then, when
they began to cry, would let them talk to a man who knew what to say.
The shadow of your absence would darken their world as your own
world was darkened. But even so, you knew there would be other Christmases, and one day a long time away from this one all that had been
fine and wonderful would be fine and wonderful again. Just not now and
for some time to come.

Abernathy, your dog, had come the closest to finding you, and
he was not even supposed to be looking. An old black-and-brown mutt
who had wandered into your backyard three years ago, you pleaded
with your parents to let you keep him, and they had agreed, if you
promised to take care of him. And you did, in your bedroom. The dog
ate there and slept there beside you. Abernathy (named after your favorite uncle) was your dog, completely. He followed you to school and waited there and walked back with you. He had been there when the man
convinced you to get in his car, and watched as you drove away with
him. He would not leave the corner where this happened, and when he
was taken back home would return to that spot, day after day. He was
still there, waiting, you were sure. The idea of it made you smile.

You could see things, even now, pictures of what was happening in your absence. It was amazing. You could see your house and your mother and father inside it and your brother in his room just lying on his bed looking at the ceiling and the pretty Christmas tree lights all dark and nothing now. But it wasn't clear really whether you were actually seeing it or were making up the pictures in your mind (or whatever your mind was now) from the crystal-clear memories you had of everybody and your life with them. You knew them so well, better than you had ever imagined. Your mother spent most of the day frozen, barely breathing. She looked like one of those wax figures in a museum. She only got up to cook dinner for her husband and son; somehow the fact that she was taking care of them made her at least partly alive, although she herself didn't eat. *Eat something*, your father said. *Just a bite.* But no. Your dad left the house before sunrise every morning to look for you, wearing his tan windbreaker and the Crimson Tide baseball cap. He didn't go to work or even think about going to work. Your brother tried not to change at all, going out with his friends, playing basketball, talking to girls. But there was a hollowness beneath his eyes, and everyone treated him kindly, worried that any minute he might just break apart.

They would never find you. You knew what was happening to you, but they didn't, and this—the not-knowing—is what would haunt them. You knew that stories need an ending and that when they didn't have one people were unhappy. People like to read mysteries—you liked to read them—but they didn't like to have them in their lives, and that's what you were, would always be: a mystery. *The Mysterious Disappearance of Alyson McCrae.* Even a long time from now the mystery of your disappearance would occur to people you didn't even know, and they would wonder about it, and shake their heads. Without an ending there was always the possibility that what everyone thought happened hadn't, that you were somewhere in the world growing up, becoming a woman, living a life. As impossible as that was, there was always that possibility. That was your last and only wish: that they knew.

Never talk to strangers. That was the rule, and outside of the house it may have been the only rule, besides looking both ways before crossing the street, and you did both of them, without fail. But he wasn't a

stranger. There were no strangers in your town; you knew almost everybody, more or less. You knew him less, but you knew him and he knew
you, enough to call you by your full name: *Alyson Philadelphia McCrae.*
Not everybody knew about the Philadelphia part. It was embarrassing,
a ridiculous name you never understood. Your mom told you once
it was where you were born, but you were born in Alabama, so that
didn't make sense. "*Began* to be born, I said," she said. And then she
smiled at you and rubbed your head. It was a pretty bad name though,
and you never told anybody ("The *P* stands *for please mind your own business,*" you had been known to say), and so he must have heard it from
your mom or dad. It was like saying a magic word—*abracadabra*—hearing him know this, assuming he knew your parents a lot better than he
actually did. Though you pretended to be curious for a minute or two
after, you never thought there could be anything wrong with getting in
his car.

"Everybody's okay," he said. "But your mom and dad had to
run down to Dothan all of a sudden."

"Grandma?" you said.

He nodded. "She's been better," he said. "All signs point to a
swift recovery, however. They just needed to get down there and make
sure the doctors don't bury her by accident."

"She's a wildcat," you said. "She'd scrape her way out, they did
that."

"You'd better believe it," he said. "Car's right here. Hop on
in."

"What about Abernathy?"

The man froze up and you couldn't figure out why. Now you
know, of course. He thought there was somebody else there, somebody
he didn't know about. "Who's Abernathy?" he asked.

"My dog," you said.

"Oh. Abernathy. I can't have a dog in the car," he said. "I'm
allergic. Can Abernathy make his way back home on his own?"

"He's the smartest dog in Alabama," you said. And you held
his small pointy head in your hands and kissed him right between the
eyes. "You go on home now Abernathy," you said. "Let's see who gets
there first."

192

But Abernathy wouldn't move. He watched you get into the car and drive away, and when you turned around to look he was still there watching, getting smaller and smaller as you got farther and farther away.

How could no one have seen this? And again not for you, because if they had it would have been way too late for you, but for your parents, for your brother, so they could have a place to set down their grief. In a town so small you knew everybody and everybody knew you. Maybe when it's like this, sometimes you're just taken for granted, invisible. Alyson McCrae wasn't news yet. She was just a little girl.

"This ain't the way home," you said. Now that you were in the car he figured he didn't have to pretend to be someone he wasn't, doing something he wasn't. He didn't have to pretend to be driving you home now.

"Maybe I know something you don't," he said.

"Like what?"

"Like maybe it's a shortcut."

"A longcut more like," you said. "You about can't get there from here."

"You sure have a mouth on you, Alyson Philadelphia Mc-Crae," he said.

"Well this ain't the way," you said.

"I think you'll see," he said, smiling over at you and driving, tapping the steering wheel with his index finger with a steady beat, as though he heard a song only he could hear.

You would see but by then it was way too late.

You kept trying to remember if you'd ever met him before as he drove out of town, past every farm you'd ever seen and then past those you hadn't. Maybe at a party your parents gave one time. That was it. "Alyson McCrae," he said. "It's a pleasure to meet you." You remembered now because he was an odd one. He was very skinny. He had a long face and right on top of it a forehead as big as Canada. His hair was thin too. You figure he had about eighteen hairs, all slicked back like they were worth the trouble. He had a small metal American flag pinned to the lapel of his jacket, which was brown. You thought you'd never seen him before but he knew your middle name so you figured there was something, some relationship, a bond between this man and your family, otherwise there is no way in the world you would have gotten into his car. No way in the world. But there was nothing you could do now.

"I don't know you," you said.

He was quiet now, driving, still drumming his finger against the steering wheel.

"I want you to take me home," you said.

But it was as if you weren't even there.

On the morning of the seventh day you knew they'd never find you. But the truth is you really didn't know what day it was: it might have been the seven hundredth day, or the seven thousandth. Maybe everybody was dead, everybody you knew and everybody who knew you. Everybody was dead, and everybody died the same way, with the mystery inside of them, the mystery of what happened to Alyson Philadelphia McCrae.

Why? How long had you spent wondering why? What did you do that was so bad? How had you lived in the world that you would deserve to die like this? You reviewed every moment you could remember—and there were a lot of moments, twelve years of them—and you came up with nothing. There was no reason. Things happened. Bad things, good things. Like Abernathy just wandering into the yard one day and becoming your warm and steady pal. And Janice, Maria, and Kristy, your three really good friends you never even met before this year. And the mother you had, and the father, and the brother—people who never let a whole day go by without letting you know in some way how much they loved you. What had you done to deserve all this sweetness?

Nothing. Things like this just happened. Nearly Christmas now it seemed, and then that car, that man, that day. There was no real difference between the whys of the love and hate. Except the love was better.

DEAR FRIEND
Rick Bragg

Dear Friend,

I never know what to say in a time of loss. Everything turns to ashes in my mouth, and words seem so trite and useless. But in such times you are moved to say something the same way you are moved to knot a choking scrap of silk around your neck and squeeze into grown-up shoes and a black coat. It is how we mourn, in Alabama. Sometimes, of course, we pitch a good drunk, but that is mostly the Catholic.

But we will have no funeral for Cormac, because he is not gone, only lost, and there is a big difference there. Most likely he is not even lost.

He is, I believe, stolen.

Somebody saw him, his fine red hair and his well-formed body and broad, intelligent head, and stole him. Sons of bitches.

Because Cormac is not a mean soul, he allowed himself to be stole.

Somebody said, "Hey, boy," and he bounced on over, and was took.

And we are left here to be sorry.

But there are some things that need to be said to you from a friend, and I have never been quiet in my life.

In his days with you and your wife and your boys, he was warm and well-fed and loved as much as any beast can be, and a whole lot better than a lot of children.

He suffered no cruelties. He was not beaten into compliance.

He lived fat and easy in a house on the hill.

The last time I saw him, with you, he literally jumped for joy.

Over and over, he hurled his body into the air, higher and higher.

It almost made me cry.

I had no luck with dogs. The wheels of cars took them, mostly. Feists, beagles, mixed-breed hounds, all perished on the Roy Webb Road. The only dog I had for any length of time died from heartworms because I lapsed in my care of him, because I was too busy. I should tell people that, when they say nice things about me.

But I had no luck, as to dogs.

So, when you told me how Cormac lay at your feet every single day as you wrote your novel, I was touched but also a little jealous. I am sorry now, for that envy.

Cormac seemed to sense that in me. He followed me around your house, insisting to be loved, and when I sat quietly in an otherwise empty room, he came in and laid his head on my knee, and just left it there.

Only when he heard your voice did he even twitch, and then he was gone, chasing the sound of your voice up the stairs.

I hope, someday, he just comes walking back up in the yard.

I hope he makes one of those miracle treks home.

I would like to think that whoever took him will have an attack of conscience, but that is unlikely. A man who would steal a dog is a low man, and it may be that all we will ever get from him is a darker satisfaction.

We will learn who took Cormac. We will not kill that man— because even though he is a thief, he may have cared for the dog, gently.

But I think we should take him to the swamp. I think we should tie him to a tree, and ask him some questions. We should scare him a little bit.

And if he laughs, or sneers, we will chop off one of his toes.

One of the big ones.

We will take him to the doctor, and leave him in the parking lot, and if he threatens us with legal harm, we will remind him that he has nine more toes.

That day, and that satisfaction, may never come. All that is left, in the end, is this.

He was not a lawn ornament, not an animal you bought to be fashionable. He had two acres of fence line to mark as his own, and he did so with great determination. When you left the swimming pool gate open, he dove right in, no matter how many times you hollered, "Cormac, damn ye," and chased him out.

He terrorized squirrels and tolerated cats. He woke your two boys up by jumping into their beds. He listened to you read to him from words you wrote. He always, always thought it was fine. He thought you were Melville. He thought you were Faulkner.

He did not, for a big dog, greatly stink.

He loved you back, all of you. You could just tell.

I envy you, still.

Your friend,
Rick

Editor's note: Happily, dognapping victim Cormac was located, far away, and returned to Sonny, who turned it all into a novel, *Cormac: The Tale of a Dog Gone Missing*.

THE CAFÉ UNDER THE TRANSOM
Jim Gilbert

Christmas 1998, Sonny Brewer invited a retired actor friend of his, Sam Busby, to do a holiday reading at Over the Transom Books. We borrowed the photography studio space next door, cobbled together what chairs we had, and set out some cookies. Sam rolled out selections from Truman Capote, Shakespeare, the Bible, a solemn, gorgeous recitation of *Silent Night*. The gathered few were reluctant to leave. "We should do more of this," Sonny declared as we swept up afterwards. "This should be what the bookstore is for."

By the next holiday season, Kyle Jennings had come aboard and Over the Transom had developed a publishing arm with a book to promote: Frank Turner Hollon's *The Pains of April*, a slender meditation on aging, *Jonathan Livingston Seagull* set in a nursing home. During the SEBA bookseller's trade show that autumn, Sonny, Kyle, and Frank were introduced to William Gay by our old buddy Tom Franklin, each there launching respective book tours in support of *The Long Home* and *Poachers*. Learning Tommy would be down in our neck of the woods around Thanksgiving, and with William in tow, an organic plan developed — *Let's paint the barn and put on a show!* — a one-night-only event featuring all three authors reading onstage, followed by an Over the Transom-hosted signing the following Sunday afternoon, corresponding to Fairhope's annual downtown "open house," when merchants ceremoniously opened their doors in the hopes of attracting early holiday shoppers (spoiler alert: it generally works, especially when they put out snacks as well).

We were told we were crazy. Three unknown, debut authors, reading *literature* on a Saturday night, not just any Saturday night but *during the Iron Bowl?* Nobody would show, no way, not even for free.

We secured use of Centennial Hall, which seats 200+ if you

include the balcony. I dreamed up a circus poster design and an eponymous moniker for the event, *Southern Writers Reading*; Sonny supplied text and soon they were taped up in shop windows all over town. Kyle rented a van to shuttle everyone around (un-wrangled writers, scattered watering holes, so forth) and Sonny ordered giant bookstore-branded magnets to slap on the doors. Crazy, whatever, we saw things lining up a certain, undeniably entertaining, way. Frank's book had sold well in the local market, serious accolades were boosting Tommy's freshly-minted *Poachers*, and *The Long Home* was to be reviewed in the *New York Times* the very Sunday morning William would be signing books at our storefront on De la Mare Avenue. We spent our energy praying for good weather.

Somewhere north of 100 souls ventured out to the reading that night, braving clear skies and scattered college football broadcasts. With Sonny as a born Master of Ceremonies on a set decorated with props borrowed from the bookstore, the evening began somberly as Frank remembered Robert Bell (author of *The Butterfly Tree*, a novel set in 1950s Fairhope) who had provided a soulful introduction for *Pains of April;* that very morning, Bell's daughter had called the bookshop to inform us of his passing. But spirits raised quickly: Sonny introduced each author by reading a particularly striking paragraph or three from their work, then asking, "Now, what were you thinking when you wrote that?" (Tommy tried to convince the audience his stories were written during commercial breaks in *Friends* marathons.) As William's thick rural Tennessee accent, song of pure earthen Southern literature, reverberated over the gathered, I thought to myself, *In ten years, it'll seem like a miracle we got this guy to read here.*

Up to that point, I'd drifted pretty casually through the 90s, book-selling at Page & Palette, endlessly scratching at a novel-in-stories, listening to a lot of surf music, not much else. I'd started working for Sonny more or less by happy accident, aggressively hanging around his bookstore until he offered me work, that sort of thing. For the past year we'd been doing used-and-rare book searches, learning valuations and rummaging like biblio-anthropologists through library and estate sales to boost our own inventory; I self-taught myself book repair, tightening hinges, rebuilding channels, loving old books back to life (including a terrific first edition/first state copy of *To Kill a Mockingbird* lucked into by Sonny at a garage sale). Now here was a kind of energy swell happening, a wave to catch at last. The question arising wasn't *Should we do this again next year?*, but rather *How can we have **more fun** doing this next year?*

Because we had, indeed, found what the bookstore was for.

As the next handful of years blurred past, Sonny toured the Southeast by way of weekend literary conferences, rooting out a network of emerging authors while his own writerly star brightened. Southern Writers Reading, which I dubbed a "literary slugfest" on our website, divided amoeba-like into two sessions, eventually spreading over two days — including for a couple years a Friday afternoon luncheon with the authors, and "Alumni Grill" reading sessions to accommodate veterans who had enjoyed themselves so much in prior years it hindered their ability to stay away in succeeding years (this included, as it turned out, William Gay). The shows leapfrogged from location to location (our favored arena being Theatre 98), but remained counter-programmed against the Iron Bowl, and always ended with a celebratory Sunday afternoon booksigning at Over the Transom, where it wasn't uncommon for Sonny to bust out his guitar and start serenading everyone within range. We hosted bestsellers and award winners, Oprah picks and heralded debuts, a few special writers with nothing more than a good manuscript and some hope. We drew audiences from around the Southeast, selling out shows in advance. We attracted benefactors who opened their homes for generously grand post-show parties, or volunteered to host the visiting authors, or both. (For the record, we rarely declined such offers.) Things turned into a pretty fine ride, no matter the direction.

At some point in there, with scribblers coming out of the proverbial woodwork, Sonny declared our bayside town "the home of more writers than readers" and soon the non-profit Fairhope Center for the Writing Arts was drawn up, a board assembled, early plans made for Southern Writers Reading to be its tentpole fundraiser, and a resurrected *Red Bluff Review* (a one-off journal Sonny had edited some years prior) to be an annual tie-in, a chapbook of flash fiction commissioned from the authors we'd feature on stage. But a funny thing happened on the way to Theatre 98...

In a story unto itself, Frank's novel had meanwhile bounced onto the desk of Pat Walsh at MacAdam/Cage, who called inquiring about a follow-up; after contracting *The God File,* Walsh and publisher David Poindexter flew over to attend that year's [2001] Southern Writers Reading events, to hear Frank read from his new book, months in advance of its publication. They got more than that; they got a full-on grassroots literary revival, three days and more than a dozen authors, reading sessions that blended from one party to the next, Grayson Capps providing musical punctuation throughout. Poindexter would later describe the experience as "falling into a nest" of wordsmithing talent. "I don't get it," Walsh confided to me after just the first night, "We do this in San Francisco, we get seven people. You do it here in this little Alabama town, and a hundred plus show up." I didn't have an answer for him then, and I wouldn't have one now, other than we picked the right battle, some kind of magic, a celestial alignment, whatever, it worked.

Sonny, long-time sailor and therefore no stranger to celestial navigation, knew exactly where to steer. The year prior, following a reading by Suzanne Hudson that had the audience howling with laughter, he declared, "I wish I could publish that," then scanned the offstage shadows for Joe Taylor of Livingston Press, in attendance that night. "Joe, is she not a writer you'd be proud to publish?" *Opposable Thumbs* had been available from Livingston since late summer. So when from the podium at the conclusion of the ceremonies, Sonny began describing a hardbound anthology featuring not only all the authors featured that weekend, but all previous SWR participants, I could feel the question gathering in the aether. "David Poindexter, does that not sound like an incredible book?" What choice did the man have?

Inclusion on MacAdam/Cage's Fall 2002 list gave Sonny a manuscript-assembling deadline of mere weeks. No problem: not only did everyone contacted gladly offer up a submission within a month of being asked, but Sonny found himself eyeball-deep in rich materi-al besides, even as the contributors list swelled to include writers who hadn't (or hadn't yet) been featured on a SWR stage. The most difficult task, then, was coming up with a properly zippy title; nothing useful suggested itself, and everyone hated everyone else's ideas, which ranged from the square-pegged *Red Bluff Reader* to simply and vaguely *Fairhope*. Finally, Frank Turner Hollon twigged on the Blue Moon Café, a ficti-tious Fairhope location mentioned in Robert Bell's *Butterfly Tree*.

An unbroken circle. Often enough in the year or so before all the literary shoutin' began, I'd drift up to the bookstore of an evening, where the bounty of some or other used "book haul" waited to be cataloged, tomes piled elbow-high in the narrow back area we dubbed the Engine Room. Just to do an after-hours repair on some volume, or key a few books into our online inventory, Zen work in the quiet lamp-light, a bubble of a moment without foot traffic or phone interruptions that could equally be spent freely leafing through generations-old travelogues, forgotten fiction, pages where the foxing was overtaking the baroque woodcuts, scandal-ridden biographies of vaudeville-era celebrities. You never knew when a treasure would flutter out of a binding: an old love letter, perhaps never sent; grandly printed opera tickets; undated photographs of mystery relatives; newspaper broad-sheets too brittle to be unfolded, their news turning to acid. Alchemic inspiration, the after-dinner hours were best for such work and discov-eries. (Also because, as every writer will tell you, there is no balm quite like procrastination.) And often enough, it wouldn't be long before I'd hear Sonny's own keys rattling at the lock. "Someone needs the Café," he'd say in greeting, tossing his longshoreman's cap atop the glass front counter. And that was the mantra. Whenever asked, strapped for time and energy as he was, devoting his mojo to numerous projects ("Busy as a one-eyed cat watching three rat-holes" was a favored description), why Sonny kept the bookstore open, that was the perpetual answer. Someone might need some well-lighted place, even if (especially if?) it

202

were only to be found within the pages of a book. That, too, is what a bookstore is for.

INTRODUCTION TO WILLIAM GAY'S *Harrikin* PAINTING
Dawn Major

"The Harrikin grew wild. Trees sprouted up thorough the works of man. Kudzu and wild grapevines climbed the machinery until ultimately these machines seemed some curious hybrid of earth and steel. Roads faded and the woods took them until there was nothing to show that wheels and hooves or feet had ever passed here. Brush and honeysuckle obscured the sunken shafts, and horses or whatever trod there might abruptly have what they'd taken for solid earth suddenly vanish beneath their feet . . . Hunters have vanished as well, folks who thought they knew the woods lose their sense of direction in these woods, even compasses go fey and unreliable. . . .

It was called the Harrikin long before the thirties when the tornado cut a swath through it. Folks called the tornado a harrikin, a hurricane, one fierce storm the same to them as another."

—from William Gay's novel, *Twilight*

"The rutted road wound down and down. Other roads branched off this one and others yet, like capillaries bleeding off civilization into the wilderness, and finally he was deep in the harrikin."

—from the collection *Time Done Been Won't Be No More,* from the short story "Where Will You Go When Your Skin Cannot Contain You?"

If Southern gothic author William Gay were alive to see his artistic depiction of his haunted, apocalyptic forest, what some have referred to as Gay's Underworld—the Harrikin— used for the back cover art of *The Best of the Shortest: A Southern Writers Reading Reunion,* he would be pleased to be in such good company, and in the company of many old friends.

Not widely known for his folk art, Gay wanted to use his art for his covers, something publishers rarely agreed to. During his lifetime he would only see his art on two covers, *Wittgenstein's Lolita and The Iceman* (Wild Dog Press, 2010) and *Time Done Been Won't Be No More: Collected Prose* (Wild Dog Press, 2010). Since Gay's passing in 2012, the William Gay Archive has been collecting both his written work and artwork. But it was not until Gay's entire oeuvre was compiled and analyzed that a connection was made between his paintings and his settings, real and fictional. Over a ten-year period, Team Gay (which consists of a group of writers, scholars, professors, editors, and fans) has diligently advocated for William by publishing five posthumous books, three of which feature his art on the covers, bringing his artwork to light.

Gay's *Harrikin* painting depicts a forest meant for darker gods, haunted by the castoffs and outcasts who refused to leave this forsaken landscape. Gay was particularly fascinated with the remnants of the old mining town, the people who remained even after the mining operations ceased in the Harrikin, leaving deep pits blasted in the landscape. First stolen from Native Americans, later stripped and ultimately destroyed for its natural resources, the once Edenic forest, having been ravished for its timber, became Gay's literary and artistic playground. Gay made it his own.

Even though the Harrikin is long gone, with Gay's paintings readers become voyeurs of Gay's prose. They now may wholly immerse themselves into his scenes, better articulate his settings, or even drive down the abandoned roads of the Harrikin with one of his most famous villains, the paperhanger:

"Even more dubious reminders of civilization as these fell away. He drove into the Harrikin, where he lived. A world so dark and forlorn light itself seemed at a premium. Whippoorwills swept red-eyed up from the roadside. Old abandoned foundries and furnaces rolled past, grim and dark as forsaken prisons. Down a ridge here was an abandoned graveyard, if you knew where to look. The paperhanger did. He had dug up a few of the graves, examined with curiosity what remained, buttons, belt buckles, a cameo brooch. The bones he laid out like a child with a Tinkertoy, arranging them the way they went in jury-rigged resurrection." (79)

There is a distinct beauty in Gay's paintings as with his language; they both encapsulate a hardscrabble determination and tough exterior, an unapologetic account of grim realism that is often dark and sinister, even otherworldly.

Whether with his hauntingly beautiful and unique prose or its spiritually/creatively connected paintings, William Gay has made an indelible mark on the landscape of Southern arts, a mark we are dedicated to preserving, with gratitude.

To learn more about the William Gay Archive and the team members, visit: About the Archive — Author William Gay

About the Contributors

Marlin Barton's most recent book is *Children of the Dust*; he teaches in the Writing Our Stories program for juvenile offenders and in the MFA program at Converse University.

Rick Bragg is the bestselling author of more than half a dozen books, including *All Over But the Shoutin'*, and is the winner of the James Beard Award and the Pulitzer Prize.

Sonny Brewer has been writing for a long time but now mostly hangs out with his little dog Bobby wondering how things would have been different had he, instead, sold life insurance.

Multiple award-winning photographer **Maude Schuylar Clay's** (front cover, dedication) books include *Delta Land*; *Delta Dogs*; *Mississippi History*, (foreword by Richard Ford); and, with poet Ann Fisher-Wirth, *Mississippi*. Her work is in the collections of major museums nationwide.

Doug Crandell, who works at the University of Georgia, is the author of eight books and is a regular contributor to *The Sun* magazine and *Ellery Queen Mystery* magazine.

Taylor Michael D'Amico (cover design) is a former actress, film producer and editor, and teacher-turned-marketing-agency-owner. For more: streetheatmedia.com

The recipient of a Bread Loaf Fellowship and the Narrative Prize, **Pia Z. Ehrhard**t, who lives in New Orleans, Louisiana and Queens, New York, is the author of the upcoming memoir *Great Falls: A Love Story*; *Famous Fathers and Other Stories*; and *Now We are Sixty*.

David Wright Faladé is the award-winning author of the novel *Black Cloud Rising*, selected by the *New York Times* and the *New Yorker* as one of the Best Books of 2023. He teaches at the University of Illinois.

Beth Ann Fennelly, the poet laureate of Mississippi from 2016-2021, is a multiple grant winner, including a Fulbright to Brazil. Her sixth book, *Heating & Cooling: 52 Micro-Memoirs* (W.W. Norton), was an *Atlanta Journal Constitution* Best Book and a Goodreads Favorite.

Joe Formichella (co-editor, contributor) is a multiple literary award winner, the author of five novels, four works of nonfiction, and his short stories and essays have been widely anthologized.

Patricia Foster is the author of *All the Lost Girls, Just Beneath My Skin, Girl from Soldier Creek*, and the forthcoming *Written in the Sky: Lessons of a Southern Daughter*. She is a Professor Emerita with the MFA program in nonfiction at the University of Iowa.

Tom Franklin, from Dickinson, Alabama, is the author of four books and co-author, with Beth Ann Fennelly, of *The Tilted World*. He lives in Oxford, Mississippi, and teaches at Ole Miss.

Robert Gatewood is an award-winning fiction writer and editor, and the founder of the Boulder Writing Studio, which twice hosted the immortal Brad Watson. He lives and writes in New York, also serving as creative director for an independent film production company.

As bookseller, librarian, and editor, **Jim Gilbert** sure makes a mean cappuccino. He is currently shaping John W. Campbell's Dianetics journals into a critique of mid-20th century American science fiction. He lives in Birmingham, Alabama.

Mandy Haynes (co-editor) writes literary fiction with a southern drawl and is the author of two award-winning short story collections and a novella. She does freelance work and is the editor-in-chief of *Well Read* magazine.

Jason Headley co-wrote Pixar's *Lightyear* and *Onward* and wrote and directed the SXSW special jury prize-winning feature *A Bad Idea Gone Wrong*.

Frank Turner Hollon and his wife Allison live in Baldwin County, Alabama, where Frank practices law and sits as the Municipal Court Judge of Gulf Shores. He has ten published novels, several short stories, and two films adapted from his work, but no longer writes for publication.

Suzanne Hudson (editor, contributor) is the multiple prize-winning author of three novels, a memoir, two collections of short stories, and her work has been widely anthologized. Her comic novel, *The Fall of the Nixon Administration*, was released in the spring of 2020.

New York Times and *USA Today* bestselling author **Joshilyn Jackson** writes page-turning suspense novels that revolve around timely women's issues. She lives in Decatur, Georgia, with her family and is an award-winning audiobook recorder. For more: joshilynjackson.com

Bret Anthony Johnston is the author of *Remember Me Like This* and *Corpus Christi: Stories*. His fiction has appeared in many places, including earlier volumes of *Stories From the Blue Moon Café*.

Abbott Kahler is the *New York Times* bestselling author of four works of narrative nonfiction, most recently the award-winning *The Ghosts of Eden Park*, a *Smithsonian Magazine* top ten history book of 2019. Her debut novel, *Where You End*, was released in January 2023.

Doug Kelley, a native of Fort Smith, Arkansas, now lives in the Choctaw Nation of Oklahoma and had a career as a corporate pilot, which inspired "Nearing Mars."

Cassandra King is an award-winning author of five novels and two books of nonfiction, her latest of which, *Tell Me a Story: My Life With Pat Conroy*, was SIBA's 2020 Book of the Year.

Suzanne Kingsbury is an award-winning author whose books have been translated widely and optioned for film. She can be found at www. gatelesswriting.com .

Southern Literary Review's **Dawn Major** is an multiple award-winning literary editor who is a member of the William Gay Archive. She is currently curating Gay's literary landscapes. Her debut novel, *The Bystanders*, was released this year. For more: www.dawnmajor.com

Bev Marshall, a military wife for twenty-two years, is the award-winning author of three novels and a memoir. She is the former writer-in-residence at the University of Southeastern Louisiana.

A finalist for the Southern Book Critics Circle Award and recipient of the Alabama Library Association's Book of the Year award, **Michael Morris** is the author of four novels.

Janet Nodar lives in Mobile, Alabama, writes about global shipping professionally, and recently began writing poetry again, after a long hiatus.

Jennifer Paddock, the author of three novels, *A Secret Word, Point Clear*, and *The Weight of Memory*, is a writer at *Tennis View Magazine*. A former #1 junior player in Arkansas, she played NCAA Division I tennis and taught it for 13 years at The Grand Hotel, Point Clear, Alabama.

Theodore Pitsios was born in the village of Tsagarada, Greece and lives in Orange Beach, Alabama. He is the author of three books: *The Bellmaker's House, Searching for Ithaca*, and *Walking in the Light*.

Lynn Pruett, who earned an MFA from the University of Alabama, is the author of one novel, *Ruby River* (Grove/Atlantic), and many short stories, essays, and agricultural articles.

Ron Rash's newest novel is *The Caretaker*, published in September 2023. He teaches at Western Carolina University.

Michelle Richmond is the *New York Times* bestselling author of eight novels and story collections. She grew up in Mobile, AL and attended the University of Alabama.

R.P. Saffire is a pseudonym. Her fictional-ish memoir, *Shoe Burnin' Season: A Womanifesto*, deals with sex, love, rock 'n roll, betrayal, the underbelly of the writing business, and literary sabotage—with humorous social commentary and bawdy poetry thrown in.

Dayne Sherman is a writer and reference librarian in Ponchatoula, Louisiana, where he lives with his family.

George Singleton has published nine collections of stories, two novels, and a book of writing advice.

Emmy Award winner **Robert St. John**, who has spent four decades in the restaurant business, is the author of eleven books, has a weekly syndicated column, and has been named Mississippi Top Chef.

The Paramount+ miniseries about the legendary African American lawman *Bass Reeves*, directed by Taylor Sheridan and starring David Oyelowo, is based on **Sidney Thompson's** novels, *Follow the Angels, Follow the Doves*; *Hell on the Border*; and *The Forsaken and the Dead*.

Daniel Wallace is the author of six novels, and a memoir, *This Isn't Going to End Well*. He lives in Chapel Hill, NC, and teaches at the University of North Carolina.

Daren Wang is the author of *The Hidden Light of Northern Fires*. He was the founding executive director of the Decatur Book Festival and a public radio producer/host with numerous credits. He's invisible now. He has no secrets to reveal.

Wanderer, poet, and literary archaeologist **J.M. White** (back cover image curator) has thirteen books in print and his next is titled *Pulling a Torch from the Sky*. He is the archivist of the William Gay estate and has helped compile and edit the posthumous works of William Gay.

James Whorton, Jr. is a novelist from Hattiesburg, Mississippi, now living in Rochester, New York.

Mac Walcott is an architect and farmer who lives with his family at Little House Farm on Fish River in Baldwin County, Alabama. He enjoys writing essays and articles for publication.

Karen Spears Zacharias descends from a Glasgow ship merchant; "The Walker" is an excerpt from her forthcoming book, *Tam O'Shanter*. She is an award-winning author of several books of fiction and nonfiction and is active in her support of veterans and Gold Star Families.

"Fools are free." —J.W. Formichella